LOCAL NEWS

1750-192

England and Wales,
Channel Islands, Isle of Man

A SELECT LOCATION LIST

Second Edition

Compiled by
Jeremy Gibson, Brett Langston
and Brenda W. Smith

Federation of Family History Societies

0885264417

First published 1987 by the
Federation of Family History Societies.

Second edition published 2002 by
Federation of Family History Societies (Publications) Ltd.
Units 15-16 Chesham Industrial Estate, Oram St., Bury, Lancs. BL9 6EN, England.
On-line Bookshop: www.familyhistorybooks.co.uk
E-mail enquiries: orders@ffhs.org.uk

ISBN 1 86006 157 5

Computer typesetting and layout by Brett Langston and Jeremy Gibson.
Printed by Parchment (Oxford) Limited.

Cover illustration: The Stanhope first all-iron printing press, invented about 1800, from an engraving of 1831. It was much used for the printing of newspapers in the early nineteenth century.

ACKNOWLEDGMENTS

Fifteen years have elapsed since the first edition of this guide to local newspaper holdings. That a new edition at last sees the light of day is thanks to several colleagues who between them have done most of the work and renewed my enthusiasm for this difficult compilation.

All the archives, libraries and record offices mentioned in the first edition were contacted by myself or (mainly) Brenda Smith to see whether their holdings had changed, and we would like to express our gratitude to all those who responded. It became apparent that considerable changes had taken place as a result of the *Newsplan* project, with far more material now available in local repositories on microfilm and microfiche. Thanks are particularly due to those librarians who went to exceptional lengths to ensure that we had detailed and up-to-date listings of their holdings.

The computerisation of the British Newspaper Library's catalogue has also provided new and invaluable information concerning the dates and publication history of individual titles.

Although we attempted to confirm the present holdings of every newspaper repository in England, Wales, the Channel Islands and the Isle of Man, there were a number of instances of important collections where no response was received to our repeated enquiries. In such cases we have chosen still to include the entries from the last edition although these may now be long out-of-date. We have also been able to include a number of smaller libraries who have now acquired their own collections of local newspapers. With the increasing availability of newspapers in microform, local holdings (and indexes) are likely to be expanding all the time. Researchers are strongly advised to contact relevant repositories to check on exact holdings (and gaps) and to learn of new acquistions.

To my regret, because of limitations of space, the bibliographic references in the first edition are no longer included, in part superseded by the *Newsplan* project. References to early county newspapers, often covering a large area, have been simplified.

Whilst Brenda Smith gathered information from scores of libraries, it has been Brett Langston who provided the impetus to finalise the guide. Of his own accord he decided to retype the whole text using Internet information and incorporating that already supplied to us direct. It is thanks to him, and modern technology, that this new edition is so vastly clearer to consult. He brought a fresh mind to its presentation, and although I have reversed some of his innovations, we are jointly responsible for the final appearance.

Finally, the compilers would also like to thank Beth Hampson, Pauline Saul and Bob Boyd for their help with the production of this booklet.

J.S.W.G.

Federation of Family History Societies Publications Ltd. is a wholly owned subsidiary of the Federation of Family History Societies, Registered Charity No. 1038721.

CONTENTS

Introduction 4

Arrangement of the Listings ... 6

Symbols and Abbreviations ... 6

England (pre-1974 counties)

Bedfordshire 7

Berkshire 7

Buckinghamshire 8

Cambridgeshire 9

Cheshire 9

Cornwall 11

Cumberland 12

Derbyshire 13

Devon 14

Dorset 16

Co. Durham 17

Essex 18

Gloucestershire and Bristol ... 20

Hampshire and Isle of Wight ... 21

Herefordshire 23

Hertfordshire 23

Huntingdonshire 24

Kent 25

Lancashire 28

Leicestershire 33

Lincolnshire 34

London 36

Middlesex 40

Monmouthshire – see Wales

Norfolk 42

Northamptonshire 43

Northumberland 43

Nottinghamshire 44

Oxfordshire 45

Rutland 46

England *continued*

Shropshire 46

Somerset 47

Staffordshire 48

Suffolk 50

Surrey 51

Sussex 53

Warwickshire 55

Westmorland 56

Wiltshire 56

Worcestershire 57

Yorkshire

East Riding 58

North Riding and York ... 59

West Riding 60

Wales (pre-1974 counties but including Monmouthshire)

Anglesey 65

Breconshire 65

Cardiganshire 65

Carmarthenshire 65

Carnarvonshire 66

Denbighshire 66

Flintshire 67

Glamorgan 67

Merioneth 69

Monmouthshire 70

Montgomeryshire 71

Pembrokeshire 71

Radnorshire 71

Channel Islands 72

Isle of Man 72

INTRODUCTION

This Guide is designed to tell family historians what newspapers have been published in any specific place and where they can be consulted. No differentiation is made, therefore, between the original paper copies and microfilms of originals elsewhere. In any case originals are often now too fragile and only microfilms may be consulted.

It must be emphasised that the Guide can only be used as a starting point, and is in no way definitive. In particular, the dates shown are covering dates only, very often with one or more complete years missing (but *not* indicated here), let alone shorter gaps. The listings are believed to be accurate at the time of going to press, but before visiting a repository to consult newspapers for a specific period, it is essential to check first that there *are* holdings for the dates required, and (if possible) book the use of a microfilm/microfiche reader.

As with the previous edition, the basis for the Guide has been the catalogue of the British Newspaper Library at Colindale. This was formerly available only in the form of two weighty volumes first published by the British Library Board in 1975. However, more recent technological advancements have facilitated the appearance of a thoroughly revised and up-to-date listing of the Library's holdings on their internet site, which is essential for consultation by anyone seriously interested in researching in local newspapers. For Scotland, see Joan Ferguson's *Directory of Scottish Newspapers* (National Library of Scotland, 1984).

Added to the basis of this wonderful collection is the information on holdings (originals and microfilms), which was generously supplied by local libraries and record offices. The other major holding of local newspapers is of course with the newspaper proprietors themselves. These are privately owned, and no attempt is made to list them here.

In order to include this vast amount of information in a viable number of pages, a great deal of compression has been necessary. The conventions and abbreviations used are explained on page 6.

One economy has been (generally) to omit newspapers which lasted less than four years – a great many survive for only a few issues. It is assumed that family historians will generally be seeking specific events, in particular deaths with related obituary notices. For this they need to know the newspapers which lasted a reasonable number of years. To a local historian a short-lived newspaper can still be of great interest and importance, but for it to coincide with an event being sought will be unlikely. Nevertheless the keen researcher will want to check these out in the British Library *Catalogue* (www.bl.uk).

Although the provincial press existed in places from the very early eighteenth century, its content was almost entirely of national and international news copied from the London newspapers. Only from the mid century did local events start to appear. Survival of these earliest local newspapers is often fragmentary and to include details of them would be misleading to family historians. Those already in existence in 1750 are shown as such ('pre1750'), but not those that had ceased by then.

The terminal point of 1920 is arbitrarily chosen. The British Library Catalogue includes all newspapers to the 1990s or later and many libraries maintain files of post-1920 newspapers.

The availability of an index to a newspaper is an enormous blessing when any search for more than a specific dated event is contemplated. Indexes to *personal names*, or obituaries or births/marriages/deaths are noted where known, but not the place/trade/event indexes which many libraries now compile. Information on new indexes is always welcome.

Newspapers are a quite different source to most of those used by family historians. Their area of circulation is dictated by commercial factors – they respect no county boundaries let alone ecclesiastical jurisdictions which define so much manuscript source material. Then, too, whereas those records were normally designed to be retained, at least for a time, and form a part of a coherent collection, newspapers are, by their nature, ephemeral. It is amazing that any have survived at all, let alone the magnificent runs in many local collections, but missing odd issues or longer gaps must be expected. It should be noted that, with early newspapers in particular, locally-held runs are often much more extensive than in the British Library.

Introduction

Researchers must also, of course, be reminded that even when items are located in a newspaper, they may not be accurate. "If it's in print it must be true" is *not* a maxim for the family historian.

In 1986 the first regional *Newsplan* survey was carried out, covering the south-west counties of England. This report identified the deterioration of local newspapers, arising from a combination of heavy use, fragility of the newsprint medium, and often inadequate storage conditions. This led to the setting-up of research projects in each region by the relevant local authorities and the British Library, and the production of the reports listed below:

Newsplan: Report of the Pilot Project in the South-West. Compiled and edited by Rosemary Wells (London: British Library, 1986). ISBN 0-7123-3057-7.

Newsplan: Report of the Newsplan Project in the East Midlands, April 1987-July 1988. Compiled and edited by Ruth Gordon (London: British Library, 1989). ISBN 0-7123-0186-0.

Newsplan: Report of the Newsplan Project in the Northern Region, October 1987-September 1988. Compiled and edited by David Parry (London: British Library, 1989). ISBN 0-7123-0183-6.

Newsplan: Report of the Newsplan Project in the North Western Region, September 1986-January 1990. Compiled and edited by Ruth Cowley (London: British Library, 1990). ISBN 0-7123-0221-2.

Newsplan: Report of the Newsplan Project in Yorkshire and Humberside, March 1988-June 1989. Compiled and edited by Andrew Parkes (London: British Library, 1990). ISBN 0-7123-0218-2.

Newsplan: Report of the Newsplan Project in the West Midlands, September 1988-September 1989. Compiled and edited by Tracey J. Watkins (London: British Library, 1990). ISBN 0-7123-0236-0.

Newsplan: Report of the Newsplan Project in Wales / Adroddiad ar gynllun Newsplan yng Nghymru. Compiled and edited by Beti Jones (London: British Library; Aberystwyth: Regional Library System, 1994). ISBN 0-7123-0315-4.

Newsplan: Report of the Newsplan Project in the London and South Eastern Region (LASER), January 1992-December 1995. Co-ordinated by Selwyn Eagle, assisted by Diana Dixon (London: British Library, 1996). ISBN 0-7123-0487-8.

Other volumes in the *Newsplan* series covered newspapers in Scotland and Ireland, and taken together they provided a comprehensive listing of surviving newspapers, showing their extent, gaps, condition and location. The regional co-ordinators recommended priorities for the microfilimng and preservation of titles, many of which have already been acted upon (with the effect of rendering many of the reports out-of-date). The successor project – *Newsplan2000* – aims to complete this work, so it seems likely that many libraries will shortly acquire films to cover the remaining gaps in their runs of titles – please keep us informed!.

For those new to the use of newspapers in family history research, there are two F.F.H.S. publications (available from the address shown on the back cover) likely to be of use.

Basic Facts about Using Colindale and Other Newspaper Repositories, Audrey Collins, 2001.

An Introduction to Using Newspapers and Periodicals, Colin Chapman, 1996.

Arrangement of the Listings

The place of publication, when occurring in the title of a newspaper, is indicated by initial only, *i.e.*, under Bedfordshire: Dunstable, 'D Chronicle = Dunstable Chronicle'. Papers are listed chronologically.

The main title of newspapers lasting several decades or more is shown in **bold italics**. Additions to or deletions from the main title are shown in round brackets, and alterations to a title are shown by a solidus, '/', *i.e.*, under Berkshire: Abingdon: 'A (& Reading)/North Berks Herald' = Abingdon (& Reading) Herald *later* North Berks Herald. Significant changes to the main title are indicated by the symbol '>'.

Place names or specific areas occurring in subsidiary titles are shown in round brackets after the main title, *i.e.*, under Bedfordshire: Biggleswade, 'B Chronicle (Sandy; North Beds)' = *Biggleswade Chronicle and Sandy Times*, later *Biggleswade Chronicle and North Bedfordshire Gazette*. The inclusion of the complete county in which a place lies, other than in the main title, is usually ignored.

Cross-references are *only* given when a place name occurs in the title of a newspaper listed under another place, not merely on grounds of proximity and likely circulation.

Dates shown (except those in brackets) are covering dates of the British Library (Colindale) holdings between 1750 and 1920. Newspapers continuing after 1920 are shown as '1920+'. The occasional newspaper already established in 1750 is shown as 'pre1750'.

Entries in *square brackets* are for holdings in other repositories. The many local library holdings are often shown as initials alongside the name of the town. Holdings in county libraries and record offices, and other major local repositories, are listed, with abbreviations, at the start of the county. If a location code is shown without any dates, then the holding is the same as for the British Library.

Symbols and Abbreviations

*	Significant gaps in holdings	Lancs	Lancashire
+	continued after 1920	Leics	Leicestershire
>	continued as	Lib	Library
		Lincs	Lincolnshire
Arch	Archives	Lond	London
Beds	Bedfordshire	Meri	Merioneth
Berks	Berkshire	Middx	Middlesex
Bod	Bodleian Library, Oxford	Monm	Monmouthshire
Brecons	Breconshire	Mont	Montgomeryshire
Bucks	Buckinghamshire	NLW	National Library of Wales
Cambs	Cambridgeshire	Mus	Museum
Cards	Cardiganshire	N.R.	North Riding
Carms	Carmarthenshire	Nhants	Northamptonshire
Ches	Cheshire	Nhumbd	Northumberland
Cumbd	Cumberland	Norfk	Norfolk
Denbs	Denbighshire	Notts	Nottinghamshire
Derbys	Derbyshire	obit	obituaries
Dist	District	Oxon	Oxfordshire
Div	Division	Rads	Radnorshire
E.R.	East Riding	RO	Record Office
Flints	Flintshire	Salop	Shropshire
Glam	Glamorganshire	Soms	Somerset
Glos	Gloucestershire	Staffs	Staffordshire
Hants	Hampshire	Suffk	Suffolk
Herefs	Herefordshire	Univ	University
Herts	Hertfordshire	W.R.	West Riding
Hunts	Huntingdonshire	Warws	Warwickshire
Illus	Illustrated	Wilts	Wiltshire
IoM	Isle of Man	Worcs	Worcestershire
IoW	Isle of Wight	Yorks	Yorkshire

BEDFORDSHIRE

Early county newspapers – see Bedford; Cambs: Cambridge; Nhants: Northampton.

[BCL = Bedford Central Library; BLA = Beds & Luton Archive Service, Bedford.]

AMPTHILL

A & Dist *News* 1891-1920+ [BCL; BLA 1910, 1912-14, 1919].

BEDFORD

B/Beds *Mercury* (Huntingdon) 1837-1912 [BCL 1837-1902; BLA 1837-45, 1858-96, 1902-05, 1907]

B/Beds *Times* 1845-1920+ [BCL, BLA, Luton Lib].

Bedford (& County) *Record* 1876-1920+ [BLA 1897-1908, 1910, 1912-14, 1916-20+].

B & Beds *Herald* 1878-87.

Beds *Standard* 1883-1920+ [BCL 1887-96; BLA 1883-1910, 1912, 1914-20+].

B Daily/B & Dist *Circular* 1903-20+.

See also Herts: Hertford, Hitchin; Hunts: Huntingdon.

BIGGLESWADE

B *Chronicle* (Sandy, North Beds) 1891-1920+ [BCL].

B *Herald* 1903-09.

North Beds *Courier* 1909-1920+.

DUNSTABLE [DL = Dunstable Lib]

D *Chronicle* (Bucks, Herts) 1856-60 [BLA, DL].

D Borough *Gazette* (Luton) 1869-1920+ [DL; BCL 1918-1920+].

D *Advertiser* 1884-1905.

See also Leighton Buzzard, Luton.

LEIGHTON BUZZARD

LB *Observer* (Linslade) 1861-1920+ [Leighton Buzzard Lib; BCL 1919-20+; BLA 1863-99].

Weekly/LB *Reporter* (Dunstable) 1878-1920+ [BLA 1910, 1912-13].

LUTON [LCL = Luton Central Lib]

L (Weekly) *Recorder* (South Beds) 1855-59.

L *Times* (South Beds, North Herts, Dunstable) 1855-1893 > Beds *Advertiser* 1894-1916 [LCL 1855-1914].

L *Advertiser* (Dunstable, Herts) 1869-77.

L *Reporter* (Herts, Dunstable) 1874-1920+ [LCL 1874-1914, 1917-20+].

L *News* 1891-1920+ [LCL].

Beds & Herts *Saturday Telegraph* 1914-20+ [LCL].

Times Midweek 1918-20+.

Beds & Herts *Tuesday Telegraph* 1919-20+ [LCL].

See also Dunstable.

Sandy *see Biggleswade.*

WOBURN

W & Dist *Reporter* [BLA 1910, 1912-14, 1919].

For other newspapers covering Beds, see also Bucks: Amersham, Aylesbury, Fenny Stratford; Herts; Berkhamsted, Hertford, Hitchin; Hunts: St. Neots; Nhants: Northampton.

BERKSHIRE

Early county newspapers – see Reading; Oxon: Oxford.

[Bod = Bodleian Library, Oxford; OCL = Oxford Central Library; RCL = Reading Central Library.]

ABINGDON

A (& Reading)/North Berks *Herald* (Oxford, Wallingford) 1868-1920+ [Abingdon Lib; OCL].

A *Free Press* (Didcot) 1902-16 [OCL].

Oxon *Free Press* 1906-16 [OCL].

See also Oxon: Oxford

Bracknell *see Wokingham.*

Clewer *see Windsor.*

Crowthorne *see Wokingham.*

Didcot *see Abingdon, Wantage.*

ASCOT

(M. Pizzey's) Monday *Midget* 1907-15.

See also Windsor; Surrey: Egham.

FARINGDON

F *Advertiser* (Vale of White Horse) 1869-1920+ [OCL].

Hungerford *see Newbury; Wilts: Marlborough.*

MAIDENHEAD

M *Advertiser* 1870-1920+.

M *Times* (East Berks, South Bucks, Thames Valley) 1895-99.

M *Chronicle* 1911-20+.

See also Windsor; Bucks: High Wycombe.

NEWBURY

N *Weekly News* (West Berks) 1857-1920+.

N *Express* (Reading, Hants, Wilts, Oxon) 1886-99.

N *Chronicle* (Hungerford, Marlborough) 1910-20+.

See also Reading.

READING

(Oxford *Gazette* &) R *Mercury* (Newbury) pre1750-1920+ [OCL, RCL; Bod 1796-1820, 1889-1920+].

Berks (Daily) *Chronicle* 1825-1920+ [RCL].

Berks *Telegraph* 1869-73.

R *Observer* (Bucks, Hants, Oxon, Surrey) 1873-1920+ [RCL; Bod 1011 20+].

R *Express* 1879-84.

R *Standard* 1887-1920+ [RCL 1891-1920+].

See also Abingdon, Newbury.

Vale of White Horse *see Faringdon, Wantage.*

WALLINGFORD

W *Times* 1882-88 [OCL].

Berks & Oxon *Advertiser* 1889-1920+ [OCL 1889-95, 1899-1920+].

See also Abingdon.

WANTAGE

W *Chronicle* & Vale of White Horse Advertiser 1876-79.

W *Free Press* (Didcot) 1902-04 [OCL].

See also Oxon: Oxford.

Berkshire *continued*

WINDSOR

W & Eton (& Slough) *Express* 1812-1920+ [Slough Lib 1815-1920+].

W, Eton & Slough Royal/Berks *Standard* 1861-65.

W & Eton *Herald* (Slough, Maidenhead) 1868-72.

W (& Eton) *Gazette* (Slough, Maidenhead) 1874-95.

W *Chronicle* (Eton, Slough, Clewer, Datchet, Ascot) 1895-1906, 1910-20+.

See also Bucks: Slough.

WOKINGHAM

Berks *Chronicle* 1771-75 [Reading Central Lib].

W & Bracknell (& Crowthorne)/(East) Berks *Gazette* 1903-20+.

W *Chronicle* (East Berks) Advertiser 1912-20+.

For other newspapers covering Berks, see also Bucks: Amersham; Hants: Andover; Oxon: Oxford; Soms: Yeovil; Wilts: Marlborough.

BUCKINGHAMSHIRE

Early county newspapers – see Aylesbury, High Wycombe; Berks: Reading; Nhants: Northampton; Oxon: Oxford.

[Bod = Bodleian Library, Oxford; BRO = Bucks Record Office, Aylesbury; OCL = Oxford Central Library.]

AMERSHAM

Bucks *Advertiser* (Uxbridge, Middx, Herts, Berks, Beds, Oxon) 1853-61 [Ealing Central Lib].

Bucks *Advertiser* 1914-20+.

See also Chesham.

AYLESBURY

Bucks *Gazette* 1821-49 [BRO; Bod 1831-49].

Bucks, Beds & Herts *Chronicle* 1822-29 [High Wycombe Lib].

Bucks *Herald* 1832-1920+ [BRO; Bod 1834-64; Herts Archives & LS, Hertford 1859, 1884, 1898-1920+].

A *News*/Bucks *Advertiser* 1836-1920+ [BRO; Bod 1853-1864].

Bucks *Chronicle* 1848-71 [Bod 1848-64].

A *Reporter* 1882-1906.

See also Fenny Stratford.

Bletchley *see Wolverton.*

BUCKINGHAM

B *Advertiser* (Winslow, Brackley, North Bucks) 1854-1918 [Buckingham Lib 1854-1920+*].

B *Express* 1865-1915 [Buckingham Lib].

See also Oxon: Bicester.

Buckinghamshire *continued*

CHESHAM

C/Bucks *Examiner* (Amersham, Rickmansworth) 1889-1920+.

C *Advertiser* 1892-1903.

See also Fenny Stratford; Herts: Berkhamsted, Watford.

Datchet *see Berks: Windsor.*

ETON

E College *Chronicle* 1863-1920+.

See also Berks: Windsor; Slough.

FENNY STRATFORD

FS (Weekly)/North Bucks *Times* (South Beds) 1879-1920+.

(Liberal News &) (North) Bucks (Flying) *Post* (Aylesbury, Chesham) 1886-93 [BRO, Milton Keynes Lib].

FS & Dist *Independent* 1907-10.

HIGH WYCOMBE

HW *Free Press* (South Bucks) 1856-62.

(South) Bucks *Free Press* (Maidenhead) 1856-1920+ [BRO, High Wycombe Lib].

W *Telegraph* 1874-78.

South Bucks *Standard* (Marlow, Slough) 1890-1914.

Linslade *see Beds: Leighton Buzzard.*

Marlow *see High Wycombe.*

NEWPORT PAGNELL

Croydon's Weekly/Bucks *Standard* 1859-1920+.

NP *Gazette* (Wolverton, Olney) 1867-1915 [Milton Keynes Lib].

OLNEY

O *Advertiser* 1906-20+.

See also Newport Pagnell

SLOUGH

S, Eton & Windsor *Observer* 1883-1920+ [Slough Lib 1883-1911, 1913-20+].

S *Chronicle* 1912-20+ [Slough Lib 1912].

See also High Wycombe; Berks: Windsor.

Stantonbury *see Wolverton.*

STONY STRATFORD

Cottage Newspaper/North Bucks *Advertiser* 1857-1909.

See also Wolverton.

Winslow *see Buckingham; Oxon: Bicester.*

WOLVERTON

W *Express* (Stantonbury, Stony Stratford, Bletchley, Towcester) 1901-20+ [Milton Keynes Lib].

See also Newport Pagnell.

Wycombe *see High Wycombe.*

For other newspapers covering Bucks, see also Beds: Dunstable; Berks: Reading; Herts: Berkhamsted, Hertford, Hitchin; Middx: Uxbridge; Nhants: Brackley, Northampton; Oxon: Bicester, Oxford.

CAMBRIDGESHIRE

Early county newspapers – see Cambridge; Hunts: Huntingdon..

[CCL = Cambridge Central Library; CRO = Cambs Record Office, Cambridge; CUL = Cambridge University Library (only Cambridge holdings included).]

CAMBRIDGE

C *Journal* pre1750-60* [CUL pre1750-1766].

C *Chronicle* (Isle of Ely, Hunts) 1770-1920+ [CCL (index BMD 1770-77), CUL, CRO 1762-1920+; Beds & Luton Archives 1823-37].

C *Intelligencer* 1793-1800 [CCL; CUL 1793-1803]

(New) C (General) *Advertiser* 1839-50 [CCL 1839-50; CRO 1841-47*].

C *Independent Press* 1839-1920+ [CRO 1837-44*].

C *Express* 1868-1909 [CCL; CRO 1868-91*].

C University *Reporter* 1870-1920+.

C *Daily News* 1888-1920+ [CCL 1889-1920+].

Cambs *Weekly News* (Newmarket, Ely) 1889-1917 [CCL 1889-1917].

C *Graphic* [CCL 1900-02].

C *Independent Press* (Ely edn.) 1903-20+ [CCL].

C *Independent Press* (Hunts edn.) 1910-16.

C *Independent Press* (Soham cdn.) 1910-16 [CCL].

Cambs *Weekly News* (Newmarket edn.) 1910-17.

Cambs *Weekly News* (Ely edn.) 1911-17.

Cambs *Weekly News* (Royston edn.) 1913-17.

Cambs *Independent Press* (Newmarket edn.) 1917-25.

Cambs *Independent Press* (Royston edn.) 1917-25.

See also Herts: Hertford; Hunts: Huntingdon, St. Ives.

CHATTERIS

C *News* (Isle of Ely) 1903-16 [CCL].

See also March.

ELY

E Weekly *Guardian* 1889-1910 [CCL].

E *Gazette* 1898-1903 [CCL].

E *Standard* [CCL 1913-20+].

See also Cambridge, Chatteris, March, Wisbech; Herts: Hertford.

MARCH [ML = March Lib]

M & Chatteris *Advertiser* 1873 > Isle of Ely *Gazette* 1873-78 > Cambs *Times* 1878-1920+ [ML 1872-1920+].

M *Advertiser* (Isle of Ely) 1903-15.

NEWMARKET

N *Journal* 1882-1920+.

N *Weekly News* 1889-1910.

See also Cambridge.

Soham *see Cambridge.*

WHITTLESEY

W *Chronicle* 1897-1900.

W *Guardian* (Isle of Ely) 1909-15.

WISBECH

[WL = Wisbech Lib; WM = Wisbech Museum]

Star in the East 1836-40 [WL; WM 1836-39].

(Isle of Ely &) W *Advertiser* 1845-1920+ [WL, WM; CCL 1855-1920+].

W (& Ely) *Chronicle*/Cambs *Gazette* (Lynn) 1858-90 > North Cambs *News* 1890 > North Cambs *Echo* 1890-1903.

W Constitutional *Gazette* (Isle of Ely) 1873-1920+.

W *Telegraph* 1880-84.

W *Standard* 1888-1920+ [WL 1888-1920+ (index BMD at CCL)].

W *Chronicle* (Isle of Ely) 1903-15.

See also Norfk: King's Lynn, Norwich.

For other newspapers covering Cambs, see also Herts: Hertford, Hitchin, Royston; Hunts: Huntingdon, St. Ives; Norfk: King's Lynn.

CHESHIRE

Early county newspapers – see Chester.

[CH = Chester Heritage Centre; CRO = Cheshire & Chester Archives and Local Studies, Chester; MCL = Manchester Central Library; NLW = National Library of Wales; SCL = Stockport Central Library; TLS = Tameside Local Studies, Stalybridge.]

ALDERLEY EDGE [WL = Wilmslow Lib]

A & Wilmslow *Advertiser* 1874-1920+ [WL].

See also Knutsford, Wilmslow.

ALTRINCHAM [AL = Altrincham Lib; SL = Sale Lib]]

A & Bowdon (& Hale) *Guardian* 1869-1920+ [AL 1904-1920+; SL 1874-1920+].

A (Division) *Chronicle* (Bowdon, Sale, Ashton-on-Mersey, Northenden, Lymm) 1892-1901 [AL 1889-90; SL 1887-90].

Ashton upon Mersey *see Altrincham.*

BIRKENHEAD

[BCL = Birkenhead Central Library]

B (& Ches) *Advertiser* (Rock Ferry, Seacombe, New Brighton, Tranmere) Districts 1858-1920+ [BCL 1860, 1864-1920+].

B *Guardian* (Wirral) 1861-69.

B *News* (Wirral) 1878-1920+ [BCL 1880 1920+].

B *Times* (Wallasey) 1879-80, 1885-87.

Rock Ferry (& Dist)/B & Wirral *Herald* 1904-09.

See also Chester.

Bowdon *see Altrincham.*

Cheadle *see Wilmslow.*

CHESTER [CCL = Chester City Library]

Adams Weekly/C *Courant* pre1750-1900 [CRO pre1750-1752, 1755, 1757-58, 1760-61, 1763, 1767-1806, 1809-45, 1861, 1867, 1877, 1880-1920+; CCL pre1750-1752, 1755, 1757-58, 1760-61, 1763, 1767-1793, 1880-96, 1898-1920+; CH 1827-30, 1832-34, 1838, 1843-45, 1880-1920+; MCL pre1750-78, 1861-1863].

Cheshire: Chester *continued*

C *Chronicle* 1775-76, 1789-1920+ [CRO 1775-1920+; CCL 1830-1920; CH 1782-84, 1802, 1806-32, 1838, 1840-42, 1880+; Hawarden (Flints) RO 1807-1909; NLW 1775-82, 1796-1800, 1810-379, 1881-82; Ruthin (Denbs) RO 1780-83, 1788-79; University of Wales Bangor 1810-13, 1818-25].

C *Gazette* 1836-40 [CCL 1837, 1839; Liverpool Lib 1836-40].

Ches *Observer* (Birkenhead) 1854-79 [CCL 1900-20+; CRO 1856-57, 1861-1920+; NLW 1897-1920; Ellesmere Port Lib 1900-14, 1915-20+].

C *Record* (Flints, Denbs) 1857-68 [CH, CRO 1857-66].

Ches/C *News* 1866-68 > C *Guardian* 1868-1920+ [CCL 1869-79].

Cheshire Sheaf [CCL 1880-1920+].

CONGLETON

C & Macclesfield *Mercury* 1858-95.

C *Advertiser* (Sandbach, Crewe) 1856-76.

C *Guardian* 1890-1920+.

C *Chronicle* 1893+ [Congleton Lib].

See also Macclesfield.

CREWE [CwL = Crewe Lib]

C *Guardian* 1869-1920+ [CwL 1869-97, 1899-1920].

C (& Nantwich) *Chronicle* (West Ches) 1874-1920+ [CRO; CwL 1875-1909, 1913-20+].

C & Nantwich *Advertiser* 1890-94.

C & *Nantwich* Observer 1908-20+.

See also Congleton.

DENTON

D (& Haughton) Weekly New/Examiner 1873-92 [TLS].

See also Hyde.

DUKINFIELD

D *Herald* 1890-1901.

See also Hyde, Stalybridge; Lancs: Ashton-under-Lyne, Denton.

ELLESMERE PORT

EP *Advertiser* 1915-20+.

Hale see Altrincham.

Haughton see Denton

HOYLAKE

(H & West Kirby) *Herald & Visitor* 1897-1914.

Deeside/H & West Kirby *Advertiser* 1914-20+.

H & Meols *Free Press* 1915-20+.

HYDE

[TLS = Tameside Local Studies, Stalybridge]

H & Glossop (Weekly) *News* (North Ches) 1856-59. > North Ches *Herald* (Glossop, Dukinfield) 1860-1920+ [TLS 1851-1920+].

H & Denton *Chronicle* 1873-84.

H (Marple & Glossop) *Reporter* 1886-1920+ [TLS 1889, 1891-1920+].

See also Lancs: Ashton-under-Lyne; Derbys: Glossop.

KNUTSFORD [KL = Knutsford Library]

K (& Northwich) *Advertiser* (East & Mid Ches) 1882-1920+.

K Division *Chronicle* 1888-92.

K Division *Guardian* (Wilmslow, Alderley Edge) 1891-1920+ [KL 1893-95, 1899-1901, 1903-08, 1910-17].

See also Northwich.

LYMM

L *Review* 1904-14.

See also Altrincham.

MACCLESFIELD

[ML = Macclesfield Library]

M *Courier* (Stockport) 1817-1920+ [CH 1811-31; CRO 1811-31, 1842-1920+; ML 1811-1920+].

M, Stockport & Congleton *Chronicle* 1842-49 [ML 1842-1848].

M *Weekly Observer* 1858-71.

M *Advertiser* (East Ches) 1868-1920+ [CRO 1920+].

M *Guardian* (Congleton) 1873-78.

M *Chronicle* 1877-1906 [SCL 1874-75, 1891-1906*].

M *Times* (Congleton, East Ches) 1898-1920+ [ML 1905-1820+].

Wednesday's *Courier* 1906-14.

See also Congleton, Stockport.

Marple see Hyde.

Meols see Hoylake.

Middlewich see Northwich, Sandbach, Winsford.

NANTWICH

N *Guardian* 1869-1920+ [Nantwich Lib 1869-87, 1889-1896, 1899-1900].

See also Crewe.

New Brighton see Birkenhead, Wallasey.

Northenden see Altrincham.

NORTHWICH [NoL = Northwich Library]

N (& Winsford/Knutsford) *Guardian* (Middlewich, Weaverham) 1861-1920+ [NoL; CRO 1903-20+].

N (& Winsford) *Chronicle* (Mid-Ches) 1889-1920+ [CRO 1885-1915, 1920+; MCL 1885-1920+; NoL 1885, 1887-1891, 1893-1915, 1920+].

See also Knutsford.

Rock Ferry see Birkenhead.

RUNCORN [HL = Halton Lea Lib]

R *Observer* 1860-68.

R (& Widnes) *Guardian* 1869-1920+ [HL 1869-96, 1898-1910, 1912-19].

R (& Widnes) *Examiner* 1870-1920+.

R *Weekly News* 1913-20+ [CRO 1899, 1901-03, 1905-1910, 1915, 1917, 1919; HL 1899, 1901-03, 1905, 1907-10, 1913-20+].

See also Lancs: Warrington, Widnes.

SALE

S & Stretford *Guardian* 1879-1920+.

See also Altrincham.

Cheshire *continued*

SANDBACH
S (& Middlewich) *Advertiser* (East & Mid-Ches) 1879-1920+.
See also Congleton.

Seacombe *see Birkenhead.*

STALYBRIDGE [TLS = Tameside Local Studies]
S & Dukinfield *Standard* 1869-1920+.

S *Reporter* 1874-1920+ [TLS].

S (& Ashton) *Herald* 1887-1901 [TLS 1887-88].
See also Lancs: Ashton-under-Lyne.

STOCKPORT [SCL = Stockport Central Library]
S *Advertiser* (Lancs, Derbys) 1824-1920+ [MCL, SCL, Wilmslow Lib 1822-1920+].

North Ches *Reformer* (Macclesfield) 1836-39 > S *Chronicle* (North Ches, South Lancs) 1840-42 [Macclesfield Lib; SCL 1837-40].

S *Mercury* 1847-51.

S/Ches County *News* (Lancs, Derbys) 1855-1912 [SCL 1869-73, 1876-78, 1880-1912*].

S/Ches (Evening/Daily) *Echo* 1883-1920+ [MCL 1887-1900*; SCL 1887-1920+].

S County Borough *Express* 1889-1920+ [SCL 1889-1920*+].

S *Chronicle* 1891-1906.

District *Express* 1895-1917 [SCL 1899-1907]
See also Macclesfield.

STOCKTON HEATH
SH *Review* 1904-20+.

Tranmere *see Birkenhead.*

WALLASEY
[WCL = Wallasey Central Library]
W & Wirral *Chronicle* 1888-1920+ [WCL 1901-15].

NB/W *Times* 1894-1900.

W *News* (Wirral) 1899-1920+ [WCL 1899-1900, 1902-1908, 1909-20+].
See also Birkenhead.

Weaverham *see Northwich.*

West Kirby *see Hoylake.*

WILMSLOW [WL = Wilmslow Library]
W, Alderley & Cheadle *Chronicle* (East Ches) 1883-88.

W & Alderley *Express* 1907-20+.
See also Alderley Edge, Knutsford.

WINSFORD [WfL = Winsford Library]
W & Middlewich *Guardian* 1875-1920+ [WfL].
See also Northwich.

Wirral *see Birkenhead, Wallasey.*

For other newpapers covering Ches, see also Derbys: Buxton, Glossop; Lancs: Warrington, Widnes; Salop: Shrewsbury, Wem; Denbs: Wrexham.

CORNWALL

Early county newspapers – see Truro; Dorset: Sherborne.

[Bod = Bodleian Library, Oxford; CSL = Cornish Studies Library, Redruth; RIC = Royal Inst of Cornwall, Truro.]

BODMIN
Cornish *Guardian* 1901-20+ [Bude Lib, CSL, Newquay Lib, St Austell Lib].
See also Launceston.

BUDE
B (& Stratton) *Directory* 1898-1907.

CAMBORNE
Lean's *Engine Reporter* 1830-55 [CSL 1812-1904*].

Cambornian 1888-90 > *Western Star* 1890-96.

Cornish/C *Post* 1889-1920+ [Bod, CSL].
See also Redruth.

FALMOUTH [FL = Falmouth Lib]
F *Packet* & Cornish Herald 1829-48 [CSL, FL].

Cornubian 1830-37 [RIC].

(Lake's) F *Packet* 1856-1920+ [CSL, FL 1858-1920+].

F & Penryn (Weekly) *Times* 1861-95 > *Cornish Echo* 1896-1920+ [CSL, FL].

F *News Slip* 1880-1902.
See also Truro.

HAYLE
H *Weekly News* (West Cornwall) 1869-1912.

H *Mail* 1912-18.

HELSTON
H *Advertiser* 1910-18.

LAUNCESTON [LnL = Launceston Lib]
L *Weekly News* (Devon) 1856-1920+ [CSL 1856-66, 1906 20+; Lnl 1856-66].

East Cornwall *Times* 1859-77 [CSL, LnL].

(L) Cornish & Devon *Post* 1877-1920+ [Bude Lib, CSL].

Cornish & Devon *Post* (Bodmin, Wadebridge & Padstow edn) 1902-09.
See also Liskeard.

LISKEARD [LsL = Liskeard Lib]
L *Gazette* (East Cornwall) 1856-74 > Western *Herald* 1874-89.

Cornish *Times* (Launceston) 1857-1920+ [CSL, LsL].

Cornish *Leader* (East Cornwall) 1904-14.

L Weekly *Mercury* 1898-1910.

MARAZION
M & Dist *Advertiser* 1920+.

NEWQUAY
N *Express* 1905-20+ [CSL, Newquay Lib].

N *Guardian* (North Cornwall) 1887-1911.

Padstow *see Launceston.*

PENRYN
Commercial, Shipping & General/P & Falmouth *Advertiser* (West Cornwall) 1867-1920+.
See also Falmouth.

Cornwall continued

PENZANCE

P (& Cornwall) *Gazette* 1839-58 [CSL].

P *Journal* 1847-50 [CSL].

Cornish *Telegraph* 1851-1915 [CSL].

(The) *Cornishman* 1878-1920+ [CSL, Penzance Lib].

(Cornish Evening) *Tidings* 1871-1920+.

REDRUTH

R *Times* (Camborne) 1867-79 > *Cornubian* 1879-1920+ [CSL 1867-1920+].

R *Independent* 1884-95 [CSL 1879-95].

Cornish/R *Effective* (Advertiser) 1909-15.

ST. AUSTELL

SA *Weekly News* 1869-95.

SA *Star* 1889-1915 [CSL].

ST. IVES [SIL = St. Ives Library]

SI *Weekly Summary* 1889-1918 [CSL, SIL 1893-1918].

Western Echo 1899-1920+ [CSL].

SI *Times* 1913-20+ [SIL].

SALTASH

S *Gazette* 1905-20+.

Stratton *see Bude.*

TRURO

Royal Cornwall *Gazette* (Falmouth, Plymouth) 1803-1920+ [CSL, RIC 1801-1920+].

West Briton 1810-1920+ [CSL, Truro County Ref Lib].

Cornish *Weekly News* 1858-77.

Cornwall *County News* 1910-18.

Wadebridge *see Launceston.*

For other newspapers covering Cornwall, see also Soms: Taunton.

CUMBERLAND

Early county newspapers – see Carlisle, Whitehaven.

[CL = Carlisle Library; CRO = Cumbria RO, Carlisle; CCRO = Cumbria RO, Cockermouth Castle, notice required, view at WRO; WkL = Workington Library; WRO = Whitehaven Record Office.]

ALSTON

A *Herald* (East Cumbd) 1875-81 [Alston Lib 1874-81; Northumberland RO, Newcastle-upon-Tyne 1874-79].

See also Nhumb: Haltwhistle.

Aspatria *see Cockermouth.*

Bowness *see Westm: Windermere.*

Brampton *see Nhumb: Haltwhistle.*

CARLISLE

C *Journal* 1801-1920+ [CL; CRO (index 1874, 1879, 1880-1920].

C *Patriot* 1821-1910 [CL 1815-1910; CCRO 1815-1908; WRO 1857-69*, 1873-86*].

Cumberland: Carlisle continued

C *Examiner* 1857-70 [CL].

C *Express* 1861-1913 [CL 1861-95].

Evening Journal 1870-71, 1885-1913 [CL, CRO].

East Cumbd *News* 1883-1910.

North Cumbd *Reformer* 1890-95.

Northern News 1896-1900.

Cumbd *News* 1910-20+ [CL].

Cumbd *Evening News* 1910-20+ [CL].

Cleator Moor *see Whitehaven.*

COCKERMOUTH

West Cumbd *Times* 1874-1920+ [WkL; CCRO].

C (& Aspatria) *Free Press* 1899-1920.

See also Maryport, Whitehaven.

Egremont *see Whitehaven.*

KESWICK

English *Lakes Visitor* 1877-1910 [CL].

K *Reminder* 1915-20+ [Keswick Lib].

MARYPORT

(Adair's) M *Advertiser*/West Cumbd *Mail* 1853-1905 [Maryport Lib].

M *Examiner* 1864-69.

M *News* (Cockermouth) 1885-1918.

MILLOM

M *Advertiser* 1876-85.

M *News* 1884-1920+.

M *Gazette* 1892-1920+ [Barrow Record Office, WRO].

PENRITH [PL = Penrith Lib]

Cumbd & Westmd *Advertiser* 1854-98 [PL 1855-85].

P *Observer* 1860-1920+ [PL].

P/Mid Cumbd & North Westmd *Herald* 1869-1920+ [PL].

P *Recorder* 1894-98.

Lake District *Herald* 1920+.

WHITEHAVEN

Cumbd *Pacquet*/West Cumbd *Post* 1774-1915 [CL, CRO, WkL; WRO (indexed 1775-1850s)].

Cumbd *Chronicle* 1876-78 [WRO 1876-79].

W *Gazette* 1819-20 [WRO 1819-26; CCRO].

W *Herald* 1831-78 [CRO, WRO].

W *Messenger* 1855-59 [WRO].

W *News* 1856-1920+ [WRO; CL 1872-1920+; CRO 1882-1920+].

W *Times* (Workington, Cockermouth, West Cumbd) 1859-67 [WRO].

Northern Counties *Gazette* 1876-86 [WRO].

W *Free Press* 1879-1918 [WRO 1879-1910*].

W *Advertiser* (Cleator Moor, Egremont) 1885-1920+ [WRO 1891-95, 1905-07, 1909-20+].

West Cumbd *News* 1918-20+ [WkL 1919-20+].

WIGTON

W *Advertiser* 1857-1920+ [CL, Wigton Lib].

Cumberland *continued*

WORKINGTON [WkL = Workington Lib]
Solway Pilot (Cockermouth) 1870-79 > W *Free Press* 1879-93 [WkL].
W *News* (W Cumbd) 1883-1918.
W *Star* (Harrington) 1888-1920+ [WkL 1904-20+].
W *Guardian* (Cockermouth) 1891-99 [WkL 1892-95*].
See also Whitehaven.

For other newspapers covering Cumbd, see also Nhumb: Newcastle-upon-Tyne.

DERBYSHIRE

Early county newspapers – see Chesterfield, Derby, Matlock.

[CL = Chesterfield Library; DL = Derby Local Studies Library; ML = County Hall Local Studies, Matlock.]

ALFRETON [AL = Alfreton Lib]
Codnor Park & Ironville *Telegraph* (Derby) 1860-67.
A (& Belper) *Journal* (East, Mid-Derbys) 1870-1920+ [AL 1870-1920+; ML 1870-95, 1896-1920+].
Mid-Derbys *Star* 1890-93 [ML 1889-93].
A & Dist *Advertiser* 1901-04 [ML 1901-05].
See also Belper, Ripley.

ASHBOURNE
A *Chronicle* 1865-70 [ML].
A *News* (Dove Valley) 1891-1920+ [DL; ML 1920+].
A *Telegraph* 1903-20+ [ML].
See also Derby; Staffs: Uttoxeter.

BAKEWELL
B *Standard* (North Derbys) 1861-70 [ML].
See also Matlock.

BELPER [BpL = Belper Lib]
B Weekly *Times* 1861-68.
B *Journal* 1870-75 [DL 1874]
B & Alfreton *Chronicle* (Mid-Derbys) 1885-1901 [ML].
B *News* (Mid-Derbys) 1896-1920+ [BpL 1896-97, 1899 1920+; DL 1903, 1905, 1912-17*].
Derbys *Telephone* 1898-1901 [DL].
See also Alfreton.

BUXTON [BxL = Buxton Lib]
B *Herald* 1842-1920+ [BxL 1842-62, 1870-95, 1897-1920+; Bodleian, Oxford 1894-1912].
B *Advertiser* 1855-1920+ [BxL; ML 1857-79].
High Peak *News* 1870-1920+ [BxL, ML].
B *Chronicle* (North Derbys, North Ches) 1888-1906.
High Peak *Herald* 1909-14 [Bxl ; Bodleian, Oxford 1909-1912; ML 1911-14].
See also Matlock.

CHAPEL-EN-LE-FRITH
CF, Whaley Bridge, New Mills & Hayfield *Advertiser* 1877-81 [New Mills Lib].

Derbyshire *continued*

CHESTERFIELD [CL = Chesterfield Lib]
C *Gazette* 1828-29 > Derbys *Courier* 1829-1920+ [CL].
North Derbys *Chronicle* [CL 1836-39; DL 1836-41].
Derbys *Times* 1854-1920+.
(Hatton's) Derbys *News* 1862-66 [CL 1864-66].
C & Dist *Free Press* 1890-93 [CL].
See also Derby; Yorks W.R.: Sheffield.

CLAY CROSS
CC *Chronicle* 1900-10 [Chesterfield Lib].

Codnor Park *see Alfreton.*

DERBY [DL = Derby Local Studies Lib]
(Drewry's) D *Mercury* pre1750-1920+ [DL, index 1840-1860; CL pre1750-1863].
Harrison's D *Journal* [CL, DL, ML 1776-79*].
D & Chesterfield *Reporter* 1831-1920+ [DL 1823-1920+ (indexed 1823-27)].
(North) Derbys *Chronicle* [CL 1840-41, DL 1836-42].
(Illus) Derbys *Chronicle* 1855-73.
Derbys *Advertiser* (Ashbourne, Uttoxeter, North Staffs) 1848-1920+ [DL 1846-1920+].
D *Telegraph* 1855-69.
Derbys & Leics *Examiner* 1873-77 [DL].
Derby Daily *Telegraph* 1879-1920+ [DL].
D (& Burton) (Evening) *Gazette* 1879-84.
D (Exchange) (& Derbys) *Gazette* 1860-99.
D (Daily) *Express* 1884-1920+.
See also Notts: Nottingham, Worksop; Staffs: Burton-upon-Trent.

Dove Valley *see Ashbourne*

ECKINGTON
E, Woodhouse & Staveley *Express* (North Derbys, South Yorks) 1897-1920+ [CL 1897-1911, 1913-20+].

Erewash *see Ilkeston, Long Eaton.*

GLOSSOP [GL = Glossop Lib]
G *Record* (Hyde) 1859-71 [GL, New Mills Lib].
C(dale) *Chronicle* (North Derbys) 1859-1920+ [GL 1859-60, 1870-1920+].
G *Times* 1869-1901 [GL 1869-97, 1899-1901].
G *Advertiser* (High Peak) 1871-72 > North Derby & North Ches *Advertiser* 1872-1901 [GL].
High Peak *Advertiser* 1881-1920+.
High Peak *Chronicle* 1906-20+ [GL 1906-08, 1910-20+].
See also Ches: Hyde.

Hayfield *see Chapel-en-le-Frith.*

HEANOR
H *Advertiser* (Langley Mill, Ripley) 1890-1917.
H *Observer* 1900-20+ [Heanor Lib].
See also Ilkeston, Ripley.

High Peak *see Buxton, Glossop; Lancs: Ashton-under-Lyne.*

Derbyshire continued

ILKESTON [IL = Ilkeston Lib]

I *Pioneer* 1853-1920+ [IL 1853-54*, 1856-57*, 1858-1920+].

I *News* 1857-58 [IL 1855, 1857-58].

I & Erewash Valley *Telegraph* 1868-79 [IL].

I *Advertiser* (Erewash Valley) 1881-1911, 1914-20+ [IL].

(Long Eaton, Heanor &) I *Journal* 1896-1900 [IL 1896, 1898-1900].

See also Long Eaton, Ripley.

Ironville see Alfreton.

Langley Mill see Heanor.

LONG EATON

LE *Advertiser* (Ilkeston, Erewash) 1882-1920+ [Long Eaton Lib 1882-96, 1898-1920+].

See also Ilkeston.

MATLOCK

[ML = County Hall Local Studies, Matlock]

M (Bath) *Advertiser* 1854-55, 1865-66 [ML 1854-66*].

M Bath *Telegraph* 1860-67 [ML 1860-68].

M *Observer* [ML 1874-76].

M, Buxton, Bakewell & Tideswell *Advertiser* 1877-80 [ML 1877-81].

M *Visiting List* 1881-1902 > M *Advertiser* 1902-04 [ML].

M *Register* 1887-90 [ML].

M *Guardian* 1902-12 < M *Visitor* 1912-20+ [DL, ML].

See also Wirksworth.

New Mills see Chapel-en-le-Frith.

RIPLEY [RL = Ripley Lib]

R *Advertiser* (Alfreton) 1864-1905, 1909-17 [RL].

R (& Heanor) *News* (Ilkeston) 1889-1920+ [RL 1891-97, 1899-1920+].

See also Heanor; Yorks W.R.: Harrogate: Knaresborough.

Staveley see Eckington.

Tideswell see Matlock.

Whaley Bridge see Chapel-en-le-Frith.

WIRKSWORTH

W (& Matlock) *Advertiser* 1858-78 [ML 1858-70, 1872-78].

Derbys *Independent* 1861-70.

Woodhouse see Eckington.

For other newspapers covering Derbys, see also Ches: Stockport; Leics: Castle Donington; Notts: Sutton-in-Ashfield; Staffs: Burton-upon-Trent; Yorks W.R.: Sheffield.

DEVON

Early county newspapers – see Exeter; Dorset: Sherborne.

[NDA = North Devon Athenaeum, Barnstaple; PCL = Plymouth Central Library; TCL = Torquay Central Library; WCS = West Country Studies Library, Exeter.]

BARNSTAPLE

North Devon *Journal* 1824-1920+ [NDA 1850-1920+, index 1850-95; Ilfracombe Museum 1868-1920+].

County & North Devon *Advertiser* 1832-48.

(Illus) Barnstaple & B *Times* (North Devon) 1855 > North Devon *Advertiser* 1855-1910.

B/North Devon *Times* (Bideford) 1859-1908.

North Devon *Herald* 1870-1920+ [NDA 1862-80; Ilfracombe Museum 1868-1920+].

Devon (Daily) *Post* 1872-1910.

BIDEFORD

North Devon & East Cornwall *Gazette* 1856 > Bideford (& North Devon) (Weekly) *Gazette* 1856-1920+.

Western *Express* (Torrington) 1877-90, 1911-19.

See also Barnstaple.

Braunton see Ilfracombe.

BRIXHAM

B Western *Guardian* 1902-20+.

See also Paignton.

CHUDLEIGH

(South Devon) Weekly *Express* 1855-1920+.

Combmartin see Ilfracombe.

CREDITON [TM = Tiverton Museum]

C (& North Devon) *Chronicle* 1881-1920+ [TM].

DARTMOUTH

D (& South Hams) *Chronicle* 1869-1920+ [TCL 1855-63, 1871-2, 1881-2; Brixham Mus 1855-63, 1869-72].

See also Paignton, Torbay.

DAWLISH

Westcott's *Local Press* 1868-99.

D *Times* 1868-1903.

D *Gazette* 1898-1920+ [Dawlish Museum].

Devonport see Exeter, Plymouth.

EXETER [DEI = Devon & Exeter Institute]

Trewman's E *Flying Post* (Plymouth) 1804-1917 [WCS 1768-1837, 1840-1917, index 1763-1835; Bodleian, Oxford 1800-19*].

Flindell's Western *Luminary* 1813-57 [WCS 1813-20; Royal Inst of Cornwall, Truro 1813-28; DEI 1813-57].

Alfred 1815-31 > Exeter *Independent* 1831 [WCS 1815-1830; DEI 1820-32].

Besley's E News 1827 > (Besley's) Devonshire *Chronicle* & Exeter News 1827-53 [DEI 1831-53].

(E) *Weekly Times* (Plymouth, Devonport) 1827-28.

(Woolmer's) E & Plymouth Gazette 1827-85 > (Devon & E) Daily *Gazette* 1885-1903 > Devon & E Daily *Chronicle* 1903-20+.

(Chambers's) E *Journal* 1856-61.

Devon *Weekly Times* 1861-1904 [DEI 1863-1901].

14

Devon: Exeter *continued*

E & Plymouth *Gazette* 1863-85.
Evening Post 1885-1902.
(Devon Evening) *Express* (& Echo) 1886-1920+ [WCS 1886-1902].
See also Soms: Taunton.

EXMOUTH
(Freeman's) E *Journal* 1869-1920+.
E *Chronicle* 1887-1920+.

HARTLAND
H *Chronicle* 1896-1920+ [NDA].

ILFRACOMBE [IM = Ilfracombe Musuem]
I *Chronicle* 1869-1920+ [IM 1872-76, 1885, 1890-1911].
Stewart's *Arrival List* 1873-74 > I *Gazette* (Lynton, Lynmouth, Combmartin, Lee, Morthoe, Westdown, Braunton) 1875-1920.
I *Observer* (North Devon) 1884-93 [IM 1887, 1890-93].
I *Weekly News* 1905-12.

KINGSBRIDGE
K *Gazette* 1855-1920+ [TCL 1857-1900].
K *Journal* (South Devon) 1867-1918.
South Devon *Advertiser* 1877-81 > South Devon *Gazette* 1881-1920+.
South Hams *Record* 1877-84.

Lee *see Ilfracombe.*

LYNTON
L & Lynmouth *Recorder* 1880-1903.
See also Ilfracombe.

Morthoe *see Ilfracombe.*

NEWTON ABBOT
East & South Devon/Mid Devon *Advertiser* 1870-1920+.
East Devon *Mirror* 1872-74 > N *Directory* (Torquay, East Devon) 1874-76.
N *News* 1888-1914 > NA *Directory* 1914.
Mid-Devon & N *Times* 1893-1920+.

OKEHAMPTON
O *Gazette* 1910-13 [WCS; Plymouth Inst]

PAIGNTON
P (& Newton) *Directory* (Torbay) 1877-80 > P *Standard* 1880-82.
(P) *Gazette* (Torquay, Brixham, Teignmouth, Dartmouth) 1877-87.
P *Observer* 1895-1920+ [TCL 1892-1920+].
P *Amusements* 1903-20+.
P Western *Guardian* 1907-20+.

PLYMOUTH [PCL = Plymouth Central Lib]
P & Dock *Telegraph* 1808-21 [PCL 1808-16*, 1817-19].
P *Chronicle* 1809-13 [PCL 1803-13*].
P (Devonport & Stonehouse) *Herald* 1826-28, 1831-76 [PCL 1826-28, 1831-60].
(Royal) Devonport (& P) *Telegraph* 1827-63.
P & Devonport *Weekly Journal* 1831-63 [PCL 1819-39*, 1846-47, 1849-57, 1859-60].

Devon: Plymouth *continued*

Devonport *Independent* (Stonehouse) 1833-91.
West of England *Conservative* 1836-52 (Devonport, Stonehouse) > Western *Courier* 1852-54.
P *Times* (Devonport, Stonehouse) 1842-58.
P *Mail* (Devonport, Stonehouse) 1852-61 [PCL 1861-62].
Western *Morning News* 1860-1920+ [PCL].
Western Daily *Mercury* 1860-1920+ [PCL].
(Illus) Western *Weekly News* 1861-1920+ [PCL 1882-1920+].
Western *Figaro* 1877-1902 [?PCL 1895-1920+].
Western *Independent* 1877-1920+.
Western (Weekly) *Mercury* 1879-1920+.
Naval & Military *Record* 1886-1920+ [PCL].
Plymouth *Comet* 1893-96.
Western Evening *Herald* 1895-1920+ [PCL].
Independent *Echo* 1897-1900.
See also Exeter; Cornwall: Truro.

PLYMPTON ST. MARY
P *Gazette* 1907-12.

Rousdon *see Dorset: Lyme Regis.*

SALCOMBE
S *Times* (South Devon) 1879-1906, 1909-18.
S *Gazette* 1910-20+.

SIDMOUTH [SM = Sidmouth Museum]
Harvey's S *Directory* 1850-64
(Lethaby's) S *Journal* 1858, 1862-88 [SM 1862-88].
S *Directory* 1868-91.
S *Observer* 1887-1920+ [SM 1891-1920].
S *Herald* 1898-1920+ [SM 1900-12*, 1920+].

South Hams *see Dartmouth, Kingsbridge.*

SOUTH MOLTON
SM *Gazette* (Soms) 1872-1920+ [Tiverton Mus].

Stonehouse *see Plymouth.*

TAVISTOCK
T *Gazette* 1857-1920+ [Plymouth Central Lib 1857-89].

TEIGNMOUTH
(Westcott's) T & Dawlish *Advertiser* 1849-52.
T *Gazette* (South Devon) 1849-1920+.
T *Times* 1856-1915.
T *Post* 1880-1920+.
See also Paignton.

TIVERTON
T *Gazette* (East Devon) 1858-1920+ [Tiverton Mus].
T *Times* (East Devon) 1865-84 [WCS].
T (Wellington)/Devon & Som (Weekly) *News* 1875-95, 1898-1920+ [Tiverton Mus 1893-1920+].
Western *Observer* (Taunton) 1876-1920+.
Our/T *Journal* 1898-1916.

TORBAY
T *News* (Dartmouth) 1911-20+.
See also Paignton.

Devon continued

TORQUAY [TCL = Torquay Central Lib]

T (& Tor) *Directory* (South Devon) 1846-53 [TCL 1848-1920+].

T *Chronicle* (South Devon) 1849-65 [TCL 1850-51, 1853, 1861-64].

T *Times* (South Devon) 1869-1920+ [TCL 1869-1920+].

Devon County *Standard* 1882-98 > T *Observer* 1898-1911.
See also Newton Abbot, Paignton.

Torrington *see also Bideford.*

TOTNES

T *Times* 1867-1920+.

Western *Guardian* 1882-1920+.

Uplyme *see Dorset: Lyme Regis.*

Westdown *see Ilfracombe.*

For other newspapers covering Devon, see also Cornwall: Launceston; Dorset: Bridport; Soms: Bridgwater, Crewkerne, Taunton.

DORSET

Early county newspapers – see Dorchester, Sherborne; Soms: Taunton.

[DL = Dorchester Reference Library; SA = Soms Archive & Record Service; SL = Springbourne Library, Bournemouth; SS = Soms Studies Library, Taunton.]

Beaminster *see Bridport.*

BLANDFORD

B & Wimborne (& Poole) *Telegram* 1874-86.

(B) *Weekly News* 1885-92.

B *Express* (Central Dorset) 1869-95.

B & East Dorset *Herald* (Hants) 1919-20+.
See also Hants: Ringwood; Soms: Yeovil.

BRIDPORT

(Illus) B *News* 1855-1920+ [Bridport Lib; Dorchester Lib 1855-97, 1899-1910, 1912-20+].

B, Beaminster & Lyme Regis Telegram (Somerset, Devon) 1865-86.
See also Weymouth.

Charmouth *see Lyme Regis.*

DORCHESTER

D & Sherborne (& Taunton) *Journal* 1791-1822 [SA 1781, 1795-1800, 1805-8, 1813+].

Dorset County *Chronicle* 1824-1920+ [Dorchester Lib; Poole LS Centre 1824-29*, 1830-45].

Dorset (County) *Express* 1855-86.

D *Telegram* 1901-04 > D *Mail* 1904-20+.
See also Sherborne, Weymouth.

GILLINGHAM

Weekly/Dorset *Record* 1890-99.

G *Gazette* 1903-04 > Three Shires *Advertiser* 1904-1920+.
See also Shaftesbury.

Dorset continued

LYME REGIS

LR *Mirror* (Charmouth, Uplyme, Rousdon) 1905-13.
See also Bridport.

Parkstone *see Poole.*

POOLE [PL = Poole Local Studies Centre]

P (& Dorsetshire/South Western/Bournemouth/ Parkstone & East Dorset) *Herald* 1846-1920+ [DL, PL].

P *Telegram* 1879-86.

P *Guardian* 1883-1920+.

Branksome & East Dorset *Herald* 1919-20+.
See also Blandford; Hants: Bournemouth.

Portland *see Weymouth.*

Purbeck *see Wareham.*

SHAFTESBURY

S *Gazette* (Gillingham, Knoyle) 1870-76.

SHERBORNE

Western *Flying Post*/S *Mercury* (Yeovil) pre1750-1867 [Cornish Studies Lib, Redruth; SL; DL; Plymouth Central Lib; Soms Studies Lib, Taunton; Truro Lib].

S *Journal* 1774-78, 1780-88.

S, Dorchester & Taunton *Journal* 1828-86 [SA].

Kingdon's S & Yeovil *News* (Milborne Port) 1858-62.

Dorset & Somerset *Standard* (North-West, South-East Soms) 1889-1908.
See also Soms: Yeovil.

SWANAGE

S & Wareham *Guardian* 1889-1920+.

S *Times* 1919-20+ [DL].
See also Wareham.

WAREHAM

J. W. Tribbett's W & Isle of Purbeck *Advertiser* (Swanage) 1880-89.
See also Swanage.

WEYMOUTH

Southern *Times* (Portland) 1852-1920+ [DL 1870, 1874-1881, 1886-99, 1908, 1917-18, 1920+].

W *Journal* (Portland, Bridport) 1856-66.

(W) (Portland & Dorchester) *Telegram* 1860-1920+ [DL 1860-97, 1899-1900, 1902-11, 1913-20+].

W & Portland/Dorset *Guardian* 1866-84 > (W &) Dorset (County) *Post* 1884-88.

Southern *Star* (Dorchester, Portland) 1888-93.

W *Directory*/(Sherren's) Weekly *Journal* 1892-1914.

W & Portland *Standard* 1906-20+.

WIMBORNE

W *Journal* (East Dorset) 1869-73 > Dorset *Free Press* 1874-75 [Springbourne Lib 1874-75].

Southern *Guardian* (Hants) 1887-1920+.

W & East Dorset *Herald* 1920+.
See also Blandford; Hants: Ringwood.

For other newspapers covering Dorset, see also Hants: Bournemouth; Soms: Crewkerne, Frome, Taunton, Yeovil.

Co. DURHAM

Early county newspapers – see Durham; Nhmbd: Newcastle.

[DL = Darlington Library; DRO = Durham Record Office; DUL = Durham University Library; GL = Gateshead Library; NCL = Newcastle City Library; NTL = North Tyneside Library, North Shields; STC = South Tyneside Central Library, South Shields.]

Auckland *see Bishop Auckland.*

BARNARD CASTLE
Teesdale *Mercury* 1855-1920+ [DL 1855-85; Bowes Museum, Barnard Castle 1897-1920+].

BISHOP AUCKLAND
BA *Herald* 1857-65 [DRO 1854-56].

A *Times* 1862-1910 [DRO 1862-65, 1867-1910*].

(South Durham &) A (& County) *Chronicle* 1866-1920+ [DRO 1868-69, 1875-76, 1885, 1887-1910, 1912-20+].

Spennymoor *Times* 1874-78 [DRO 1874-76, 1878].

A *Mercury* (Weardale, Teesdale, West Durham) 1875-1878 [DRO 1875-76, 1878].

A *Advertiser* 1902-05.

See also Stanley; Yorks N.R.: Middlesbrough.

BLAYDON
B *Courier* 1905-20+ [Gateshead Lib].

CHESTER-LE-STREET
CS *Liberal* 1856-71.

CS *Times* (Houghton-le-Spring) 1870-87.

CS *Chronicle* 1913-20+ [Gateshead Lib 1911-20+].

Cleveland *see Hartlepool, Stockton-on-Tees.*

CONSETT
C *Guardian* 1860-1920+ [DUL 1899, 1914; Gateshead Lib 1914-20+].

C (& Stanley) *Chronicle* (North West Durham) 1888-1920+ [DRO 1888-90; Gateshead Lib 1914-20+].

DARLINGTON [DL = Darlington Lib]
D & Stockton *Times* 1847-1920+ [DL 1847-54, 1858-76*, 1879-1920+, index 1880-on]

D *Telegraph* 1854-65 [DL 1854-55, 1858-65].

D *Mercury* 1864-72 [DL 1773*, 1868*, 1872*].

D & Stockton *Telegraph* (Richmond, South Durham, North Yorks) 1867-73 > D & Richmond *Herald* 1873-1880.

Northern *Echo* 1870-1920+ [DL & partial index; DRO 1875-1917]

Northern *Standard* (North Yorks) News 1881-87.

North *Star* 1881-1920+ [DL].

Northern/Evening *Despatch* 1914-20+ [DL, index].

DURHAM
D (County) *Advertiser* 1814-1920+ (indexed 1814-35) [DRO; DUL, NCL 1814-37; GL 1814-20].

D *Chronicle* 1820-1920+ [DRO 1820-23, 1838-41, 1846, 1849-53, 1855, 1857-1920+; DUL 1820-1915; NCL 1820, 1859-62].

FELLING
F *Gazette* 1880-89 [Gateshead Lib].

Heslop's Local/F *Advertiser* [Gateshead Lib 1903-16; Newcastle City Lib 1914-1920+].

GATESHEAD [GL = Gateshead Lib]
G (& County of Durham) *Observer* 1837-86 [GL, index; DUL 1852; NCL 1837-50, 1870].

G Weekly/G-upon-Tyne *Tribune* (North Durham) 1869-1872 [GL 1870-72].

G *Guardian* (Newcastle) 1895-1900 [GL, index to 1898].

HARTLEPOOL [HL = Hartlepool Lib]
H *Free Press* (West Hartlepool) 1855-72 [HL].

South Durham & Cleveland *Mercury* 1865-1906 [HL; DRO 1870-1906].

South Durham *Herald* (Stockton) 1866-91 [HL; DRO 1868].

(Northern) *Scribe* 1881-85.

Northern Evening/Daily *Mail* (South Durham, North Yorks) 1883-1920+ [HL].

Northern *Guardian* 1891-1902 [HL 1895-1901].

Weekly *Journal* 1901-09.

See also Stockton-on-Tees, Sunderland.

Hetton *see Seaham.*

Houghton-le-Spring *see Chester-le-Street, Seaham.*

JARROW
J *Chronicle* (Tyneside) 1870-71 > J *Express* 1873-1920 [NTL 1877-1920; STC 1871, 1873-1913].

J *Guardian* (Tyneside) 1872-1913 [NTL 1891-1912; STC 1872-80].

Murton *see Seaham.*

Norton *see Sunderland.*

Rainton *see Seaham.*

SEAHAM
North-Eastern *News* 1858 > S *Observer* 1858-70.

Seaham *Weekly News* (Seaton, Murton, Hetton, Rainton, Houghton-le-Spring) 1860-1920+ [DRO 1912].

See also Sunderland.

Seaton *see Seaham.*

SOUTH SHIELDS
North & SS *Gazette* (Nhumb) 1849-63 [STC].

Shields *Advocate* 1855-57 [STC 1855-58].

(North & South) Shields (Daily) *Gazette* 1855-1920+ [STC; NTL 1849, 1852-63].

SS *Evangelist* 1874-77 [STC].

Free Press 1806-1004 [STC 1895-97, 1899-1904]

See also Sunderland.

Spennymoor *see Bishop Auckland.*

STANLEY
S *News* (Auckland, North West Durham) 1912-20+ [DRO 1914-20+; GL 1912-14].

See also Consett.

Co. Durham *continued*

STOCKTON-ON-TEES
S & Hartlepool *Mercury* (Middlesbrough) 1855-65.

S (& Thornaby/Tees-side) *Herald* (South Durham, Cleveland) 1858-1920+ [DRO 1868].

(Middlesbrough &) S *Gazette* 1860-76 > (North-Eastern/Northern) *Weekly Gazette* (Hartlepool, Cleveland) 1876-1920+.

S *Journal* (Norton) 1880-84.

See also Darlington, Hartlepool, Sunderland; Yorks N.R.: Middlesbrough.

SUNDERLAND [SL = Sunderland Lib]
S (& Durham County) (Daily) *Herald* 1831-1902 > S *Daily Post* 1902-06 [SL; DUL 1831-76].

Northern/S (Weekly) *Times* (Hartlepool, Stockton, Middlesbrough, Shields, Seaham) 1839-90 > (S) *Weekly Echo* 1881-1914 [SL].

S *News* 1851-55 [SL].

S (Penny) *Weekly News* 1865-68.

S *Daily Echo* 1873-1920+ [SL].

S *Daily Post* 1876-81 [SL].

S Morning *Mail* 1898-1901.

Teesdale *see Barnard Castle, Bishop Auckland.*

Teesside *see Stockton-on-Tees.*

Tyneside *see Jarrow.*

Weardale *see Bishop Auckland.*

West Hartlepool *see Hartlepool.*

For other newspapers covering Durham, see also Nhumb: Newcastle-upon-Tyne; Yorks N.R.: Ripon.

ESSEX

Early county newspapers – see Chelmsford, Colchester; Herts: Hertford; Suffolk: Ipswich.

[ChL = Chelmsford Library; CoL = Colchester Library; CRO = Chelmsford Record Office; DV = Valence House Museum, Dagenham; WFA = Waltham Forest Archives & Local Studies, Walthamstow.]

BARKING
B & East Ham (& Ilford) *Advertiser* (Upton Park, Dagenham) 1888-1920+ [DV, Stratford Lib].

B & East Ham *Standard* (Dagenham, Rainham) 1895-1902 [DV].

B *Chronicle* 1911-20+.

See also Ilford, West Ham.

Bocking *see Braintree.*

BRAINTREE
B & Bocking *Advertiser* 1868-1920 [CoL 1859-60; CRO 1861-64].

B *Gazette* 1891-1906.

BRENTWOOD
B *Gazette* (Mid-Essex) 1919-20+.

BUCKHURST HILL
BH & Chingford *Advertiser* 1898-1920+.

Essex *continued*

BURNHAM-ON-CROUCH
BC & Dengie Hundred *Advertiser* 1904-20+ [CRO 1904-1909, 1916-20+].

See also Maldon.

Cann Hall *see Leyton, Leytonstone, West Ham.*

CHELMSFORD [ChL = Chelmsford Lib]
C (& Colchester)/Essex (County) *Chronicle* 1768-1920+ [ChL 1764-1920+; CoL 1811-12, 1814, 1910-18; CRO 1764-1868 (indexed 1798-1802, 1807-19)].

Essex *Herald* 1812-1920+ [CRO 1800-03, 1811-19, 1829-30].

Essex *Weekly News* 1862-1920+ [ChL; CRO 1861-66, 1868-1920+].

(South) Essex *Independent* 1862-1920.

Essex (Halfpenny) *Newsman* 1870-1920+.

See also Colchester.

Chingford *see Buckhurst Hill, Walthamstow.*

CLACTON-ON-SEA
C *News* 1889-92, as East Essex *Advertiser* 1893-1920+.

C *Gazette* (Harwich, Dovercourt) 1894-99.

C *Graphic* (as East Coast Illus *News* 1907-19) 1899-1920+.

(Illus) C *News* 1911-14.

C *Times* (East Essex) 1913-20+.

See also Walton-on-the-Naze.

COLCHESTER [CoL = Colchester Lib]
C (& Chelmsford) *Gazette* 1821-37 [CoL 1814-25, 1835-1838].

C, Chelmsford & Ipswich *Gazette* 1837-41 [CoL].

Essex (County) *Standard* 1831-1920+ [CoL; CRO 1831-1905].

Essex & Suffolk *Times* (Chelmsford, Ipswich) 1837-41.

Essex/East & West Suffolk *Gazette* 1852-73.

Essex (County) *Telegraph* (Chelmsford) 1858-1920+ [CoL 1858-60, 1866, 1879-1920+].

C *Mercury* (North Essex) 1868-1901 [CoL 1868-70, 1873-95].

Essex/C *Times* 1870-72 > Essex *Journal* 1872-76 (Harwich, Dovercourt).

C *Chronicle* 1876-92.

C *Gazette* 1877-1920+.

See also Chelmsford; Suffk: Ipswich.

Colne Valley *see Halstead.*

Dagenham *see Barking.*

Dengie *see Burnham-on-Crouch, Maldon.*

Dovercourt *see also Clacton-on-Sea, Colchester, Harwich, Walton-on-the-Naze.*

EAST HAM [SL = Stratford Lib]
EH *Express* 1892-99.

(Manor Park, Ilford &) EH *Echo* 1895-1920+ [SL].

EH *Mail* 1903-20+.

EH *Recorder* 1912-20+.

See also Barking, West Ham.

Essex *continued*

EPPING

E/West Essex *Gazette* (Loughton, Ongar) 1901-20+.

E *Advertiser* 1898-1920+.

See also Woodford.

FOREST GATE

FG *Gazette* (Stratford, Upton) 1888-1902.

See also Stratford.

GRAYS [GL = Grays Lib]

G & Tilbury *Gazette* (Southend) 1884-1920+ [GL].

G & Tilbury *Standard* 1892-98.

HALSTEAD

H *Gazette* (North Essex) 1857-1920+.

(East) (Essex &) H *Times* (Haverhill, Colne Valley) 1861-1920+ [CRO 1865-1920].

Harrow Green *see also Leytonstone, Walthamstow.*

HARWICH

H, Dovercourt (& Essex Halfpenny) *Newsman* 1870-1920+.

H & Dovercourt *Free Press* 1884-1906.

H & Dovercourt *Standard* 1906-20+.

See also Clacton-on-Sea, Colchester, Walton-on-the-Naze.

Haverhill *see Halstead, Saffron Walden.*

ILFORD

Eastern Counties' *Advertiser* 1893-1902 > Eastern Counties *Times* (South Essex, Barking) 1913-20+.

Essex (& Middlesex) *Guardian* 1894-1908.

I *Guardian* 1898-1920+.

I *Recorder* 1902-20+.

I *Gazette* 1904-07.

The *Bugle* 1907-20+

See also Barking, East Ham, Romford.

Leigh-on-Sea *see Southend-on-Sea.*

LEYTON

L *Free Press* (Cann Hall) 1893-97 [WFA].

L & Leytonstone *Advertiser* 1909-14.

See also Leytonstone, Walthamstow.

LEYTONSTONE

Leyton & L *Independent* 1877-83 > L *Express* 1883-1920+ [WFA 1884-1920+].

L *Free Press* 1903-08.

L, Harrow Green & Cann Hall *Advertiser* 1898-1903.

See also Leyton, Wanstead, Walthamstow.

LOUGHTON

L & Dist *Advertiser* 1887-1920+.

See also Epping.

MALDON

M *Express* (Burnham, Southminster, Dengie Hundred) 1872-1920+.

M *Advertiser* 1910-16.

Manor Park *see East Ham.*

Ongar *see Epping.*

Plaistow *see Stratford.*

Prittlewell *see Southend-on-Sea.*

Rainham *see Barking.*

Rayleigh *see Southend-on-Sea.*

Rochford *see Southend-on-Sea.*

ROMFORD

Essex *Times* 1866-1920+.

R & Ilford *Express* 1894-1908 [Bodleian Lib, Oxford 1894-1908].

R *Times* 1913-20+.

SAFFRON WALDEN

SW *Weekly News* 1889-1920+ [Cambridge Lib].

SW *Gazette* 1891-95.

SW *Weekly News* (Haverhill ed.) 1913-20+.

Shoebury *see Southend-on-Sea.*

SOUTHEND-ON-SEA

S *Standard* 1873-1920+.

SS *Observer* (Rochford, Rayleigh, South-East Essex) 1880-1920+ [Southend RO 1889-1920+].

S *Echo* (Prittlewell, Leigh, Shoebury, Rochford, Westcliff) 1894-1900.

S *Telegraph* (Leigh, Shoeburyness) 1900-20+.

S (Leigh) & Westcliff *Graphic* 1907-18.

See also Grays.

Southminster *see Maldon.*

STRATFORD

S *Mercury* 1869-73.

S (Forest Gate & Plaistow/South Essex) *Advertiser* (West Ham) 1878-85.

S *Times* (Bow, Bromley, South Essex Gazette) 1895-1906.

See also Forest Gate, West Ham.

Tilbury *see Grays.*

Upton Park *see Barking, Forest Gate, West Ham.*

Waltham Abbey *see Herts: Cheshunt.*

WALTHAMSTOW

W *Chronicle* (Leyton) 1872-76.

W & Leyton *Guardian* 1876-1920+.

W *Express* 1882-99.

Eastern *Mercury* 1887-1920+.

W *Herald* 1892-93.

Walthamstow (Loyton, Leytonstone & Dist) *Weekly* (Herald) 1912-16 [WFA 1892-99].

W & Leyton *Herald* 1893-1900.

W *Reporter* 1894-1908 [WFA].

District *Times* (Leyton, Leytonstone, Harrow Green, Wanstead, Woodford, Chingford) 1901-14 [WFA].

W *Recorder* 1903-06 [WFA 1903-05].

[WFA has 'local newspaper index', c 10,000 entries.]

WALTON ON THE NAZE

W (& Clacton) *Gazette* (Harwich, Dovercourt) 1878-1920.

WANSTEAD

W *Mail* (Leytonstone) 1900-03.

See also Walthamstow.

Essex *continued*

Westcliff *see Southend-on-Sea.*

WEST HAM
(Borough of WH, East Ham) & Stratford *Express* (East London, South Essex) 1866-1920+ [Stratford Lib 1858-1920+, index 1885-1909].

(County Borough of) WH *Guardian* 1888-1902.

East & WH/South Essex *Gazette* (Upton Park) 1888-91 > WH *Herald* 1892-99 > (Borough of) (WH &) South Eassex *Mail* (East Ham, Barking) 1899-1920+.

Essex *Courier* 1891-1902.

WH *Times* (Cann Hall) 1894-99.

Courier & Borough of WH News 1895-99.

See also Stratford.

WOODFORD
W *Times* 1869-1902.

W *Mail* (South Essex) 1897-1907.

W *Times* (Epping Forest) 1902-20+.

W & Dist *Advertiser* 1906-20+.

See also Walthamstow.

For other newspapers covering Essex, see also Herts: Bishop's Stortford, Hertford; Kent: Gravesend; London: London (City of); Middx: Tottenham; Suffk: Ipswich, Sudbury.

GLOUCESTERSHIRE and BRISTOL

Early county newspapers – see Bristol, Cheltenham, Gloucester.

[BCL = Bristol Central Library; GL = Gloucester Library.]

Avonmouth *see Bristol.*
Berkeley *see Dursley, Thornbury.*
Bishopston *see Bristol.*
Blakeney *see Lydney.*

BRISTOL
Felix Farley's B *Journal* 1752-1853 [BCL].

Sarah Farley's B *Journal* 1781-96 [BCL 1777-99].

B *Gazette* 1770-1872 [BCL 1771-1872].

Bonner & Middleton's/Fenley & Sheppard's B *Journal* 1774-1804 > (B) *Mirror* 1811-64 [BCL].

B (Daily) *Mercury* 1806-1909 [BCL 1790-98, 1804-1909].

B *Observer* (Gloucester, Monmouth, Somerset, Wilts) 1819-23 [BCL].

B *Standard* 1839-42 [BCL].

(Daily) B *Times* (Bath) 1839-1920+ [BCL].

(B Weekly News &) Great Western *Advertiser* 1844-47.

Clifton *Directory* 1850-51 > Clifton *Chronicle* 1852-1920+ [BCL 1852-1916].

B *Advertiser* 1855-59 [BCL 1856-59].

Western *Daily Press* 1858-1920+ [BCL].

B/Penny *Observer* 1859-1920+ [BCL 1859-60, 1866-89].

B *Daily Post* 1860-78.

Observer (Chippenham, Tetbury, Malmesbury, Swindon, Cirencester, Stroud, Wotton-under-Edge) 1874-78.

B *Evening News* 1877-1920+ [BCL 1877-97].

Bristol *continued*

B *Weekly Mercury* 1878-1909.

(B) *Magpie* 1882-1911.

Clifton & Redland *Free Press* 1890-1920+.

Clifton *Society* 1890-1916.

Bedminster Guardian 1897-1902 > B *Guardian* (Avonmouth) 1902-20+ [BCL 1897-1920+].

Holfield & Bishopston *Record* (Montpelier) 1898-1920+.

B *Echo* 1901-09.

(B) *Evening Times* 1904-20+.

Western *Weekly Post* 1909-14.

Bedminster, Knowle & Brislington *Record* 1909-10 > South B *Free Press* 1910-20+.

B *Express* 1911-15.

Avonmouth *Mail* 1912-20+.

North Somerset *Gazette* (Keynsham, Saltford, Twerton, Bath) 1913-20+.

South Glos *Gazette* (Shirehampton, Avonmouth) 1913-1920+.

See also Soms: Bath, Taunton.

CHELTENHAM [CL = Cheltenham Lib]
C *Chronicle* 1810-1920+ [CL 1809-14, 1844-47, 1913-1920+; GL index 1900-20+].

C *Journal* 1824-68.

(C) *Looker-On* 1833-1913, 1919-20 [CL 1833-1920, index].

C *Free Press* 1834-1908 [CL].

C *Examiner* (Gloucester, Stroud, Tewkesbury) 1839-1913.

C *Mercury* 1855-1903.

C *Times* 1860-72.

C *Express* 1866-88.

C *Telegraph* 1868-77.

Evening (Express) *Telegram* 1874-82.

Glos *Echo* 1884-1920+ [CL 1914-20+].

See also Gloucester; Soms: Bath

Chipping Camden *see Moreton-in-Marsh.*
Chipping Sodbury *see Thornbury.*

CINDERFORD
(Drybrook &) C *Journal* (Ruardean, Mitcheldean, East Dean, Forest of Dean) 1868-69, 1874-91.

Dean Forest *Mercury* 1882-1920+.

See also Coleford.

CIRENCESTER
Wilts & Glos *Standard* 1837-1920+ [Bingham Lib, Cirencester 1856-71, 1893-1920+].

C *Times* 1856-71.

See also Bristol, Stroud.

Clifton *see Bristol.*

COLEFORD
Monmouth *Telegraph* (Gloucester, Cinderford) 1863-69.

C (Weekly) *Times* 1863-93.

The *Forester* 1870-84.

Dean Forest *Guardian* 1885-1920+.

See also Monm: Monmouth.

Gloucestershire continued

Dean (Forest of) see Cinderford, Coleford, Lydney; Herefs: Ross-on-Wye; Monm: Monmouth.

DURSLEY

D (Berkeley & Sharpness) *Gazette* (Wotton-under-Edge) 1878-1920+ [Bodleian Lib, Oxford 1878-87].

East Dean see Cinderford.

GLOUCESTER [GL = Gloucester Lib]

G *Journal* pre1750-1920+ [BCL].

G *Gazette* 1792-96.

G (& Cheltenham) *Herald* 1802-21 [GL 1802-28*].

G *Chronicle* 1833-1920+.

G *Free Press* > G *Mercury* 1856-84 [GL 1863-66].

G *Standard* 1872-1902 [GL].

The *Citizen* 1877-1920+ [GL 1876-1920+. index].

See also Bristol, Cheltenham, Coleford.

Holfield see Bristol.

LYDNEY

Monmouthshire *Chronicle* (Hereford, Gloucester, Forest of Dean, South Wales) 1875-84.

West of England *Observer* (South Wales) 1875-1914.

(Forest of Dean News &) L *Observer* (Newnham, Blakeney) 1875-1920+.

Foresters' Halfpenny/Provincial *News* 1877-1914.

Mitcheldean see Cinderford; Herefs: Ross-on-Wye.

Montpelier see Bristol.

MORETON-IN-MARSH

(Campden Herald &) M *Free Press* 1868-96.

See also Stow on the Wold.

NEWENT

N *Reporter* 1904-1920+.

See also Herefs: Ross-on-Wye.

Newnham see Lydney.

Redland see Bristol.

Ruardean see Cinderford.

Sharpness see Dursley.

Shirehampton see Bristol.

STOW-ON-THE-WOLD

SW *News* (Moreton) 1869, 1879-95.

STROUD

S *Free Press* 1850-55.

S *Journal* (Cirencester) 1854-1920+.

S *News* 1867-1920+ [Gloucester Lib 1872-1920+].

S *Weekly Press* 1898-1901.

See also Bristol, Cheltenham.

TETBURY

T *Advertiser* (Malmesbury) 1884-1911.

See also Bristol.

TEWKESBURY

T *Weekly Record* 1855-1920+ [Glos RO 1880-1920+].

T *Register* 1858-1920+ [GL 1858-86, Bodleian Lib, Oxford 1903-20].

Tewkesbury continued

T *Mail* 1904-14.

See also Cheltenham.

THORNBURY

South Glos *Chronicle* (Chipping Sodbury, Berkeley) 1911-20+.

Wotton-under-Edge see Bristol, Dursley.

For other newspapers covering Glos, see also Herefs: Hereford; Wilts: Chippenham; Monm: Chepstow.

HAMPSHIRE

Early county newspapers – see Portsmouth, Southampton, Winchester; Wilts: Salisbury.

[BCL = Bournemouth Central Library; PCL = Portsmouth Central Library; SCL = Southampton Central Library; SL = Springbourne Library, Bournemouth – holdings may be transferred to BCL; SAS = Southampton Archives Services.]

ALDERSHOT

(Sheldrake's) A (Military) *Gazette* 1859-1920+.

Hants & Surrey *Times* 1884-95.

May's A Camp *Gazette* 1886-95.

A *News* 1894-1920+ [Aldershot Lib].

See also Surrey: Guildford.

Alresford see Winchester.

ALTON

A *Advertiser* (East Hants) 1874-77.

(North & East) Hants *Herald* 1885-1920+.

A *Mail* 1899-1920+.

See also Winchester.

ANDOVER

A *Advertiser* (North West Hants) 1858-1920+.

North Hants *Telegraph* (Basingstoke, Stockbridge, Whitchurch) 1861-70.

A *Chronicle* 1870-81.

A *Standard* (North Hants) 1881-1914.

A *Times* (Wilts, Berks) 1910-14.

BASINGSTOKE [BL = Basingstoke Lib]

Hants & Berks *Gazette* (Middx, Surrey) 1878-1920+ [BL].

B *Standard* (North Hants) 1882-85.

Hants *Observer* 1903-16 [BL].

See also Andover, Winchester.

Bishops Waltham see Winchester.

BOURNEMOUTH

[BCL = Bournemouth Lib; SL = Springbourne Lib]

B Visitor's *Directory* (Poole, Christchurch) 1868-1919 > B *Times* 1919-20+ [BCL].

B *Observer* 1875-1901 [SL 1875-1908].

Observer & Chronicle (Dorset) 1881-1909.

B *Guardian* (Dorset) 1883-1920+ [BCL 1883-95, 1897-1910, 1912-20+].

B *Daily Echo* 1900-20+ [BCL].

Hampshire: Bournemouth *continued*

B *Graphic* 1902-20+ [BCL, SL].
New Forest *Chronicle* (South & West Hants) 1919-20+.
See also Southampton; Dorset: Christchurch, Poole;
Soms: Yeovil.

CHRISTCHURCH [SL = Springbourne Lib]
C *Times* 1858-1920+ [BCL 1858-1918].
C *News* 1872 > C & Bournemouth *Chronicle*
(Ringwood) 1872-76 [SL 1872-73, 1874].
See also Bournemouth, Lymington.

EASTLEIGH [EL = Eastleigh Lib]
E *Gazette* [EL 1892-94].
E *Weekly News* 1895-1920+ [EL 1892-1920+].

EMSWORTH
(Hants & Sussex) *County Press* (Havant) 1895-1920+.

Farnborough *see Surrey: Guildford.*

FLEET
F *News* (Odiham, Hartley Wintney) 1904-20+.

Fordingbridge *see Lymington.*
Freemantle *see Southampton.*

GOSPORT
G & County *Journal* 1905-13.
See also Portsmouth.

Hartley Wintney *see Fleet.*
Havant *see Emsworth.*

LYMINGTON
L (& IoW/South Hants) *Chronicle* (Ringwood,
Fordingbridge, Christchurch) 1857-77, 1880-1920+.
Bright's L *Courier* (IoW) 1866-69.
L *Observer* (IoW) 1878-81.
(Ringwood &) New Forest *Chronicle* (Christchurch,
Fordingbridge) 1905-20+.

Millbrook *see Southampton.*
New Forest *see Bournemouth, Lymington.*
Odiham *see Fleet.*

PETERSFIELD
P *Express* (East Hants, West Sussex) 1864-1902.
Hants & Sussex *News* 1892-1920+.

Portsea *see Portsmouth.*

PORTSMOUTH [PCL = Portsmouth Central Lib]
P *Gazette* 1793-1802.
P/Mottley's/Hants *Telegraph* (Sussex) 1799-1920+ [PCL
(indexed 1799-1920+); Chichester Lib 1820-39; West
Sussex RO, Chichester 1817-18; Gosport Lib 1799-
1862; SCL 1819-22; Waterlooville Lib 1799-1868].
Hants *Courier* (Portsea, Gosport, Chichester) 1810-16
[SCL 1812-16].
P, Portsea & Gosport *Herald* 1829-35.
Hants *Guardian* (Portsmouth, Gosport, IoW) 1846-50.
Port of P *Guardian* (Portsea Island, IoW) 1850-56
P *Times* 1850-1920+ [PCL].
P *Guardian* (IoW, Gosport) 1861-68.

Portsmouth *continued*

Southsea *Observer* 1874-76 > Hants *Post* 1876-1913
[PCL 1877-1913].
Evening News 1878-1920+ [PCL].
(Evening/Southern Daily) *Mail* (IoW, Sussex) 1884-1905
[PCL 1894-1904].
Chat 1884-1920+.
Hants *County Times* 1885-1920+.
(P) *Herald* 1887-95.
Our *Gazette* 1888-93.
P *Times* 1898-1920+.
See also Southampton.

RINGWOOD
R, Blandford & Wimborne *Telegram* 1862-69.
See also Christchurch, Lymington.

ROMSEY
R *Register* 1859-94.
(R &) South Hants *Chronicle* 1874-87.

Shirley *see Southampton.*

SOUTHAMPTON [SCL = Southampton Central Lib]
S (Town & Country) *Herald* (IoW) 1823-27 > Hants
Advertiser (Salisbury) 1827-1920+ [Eastleigh Lib
1823-53; SCL 1823-27, 1854-1920+].
Hants *Independent* 1836-1920+ [SCL 1836, 1838-44,
1846-1920+].
S *Times* (Winchester, Portsmouth, IoW) 1860-1920+
[SCL; SAS 1862-1920+].
S *Observer* (Winchester) 1867-1906 > *News & Views*
1906-07 [SCL 1869-1907; SAS 1894, 1901-06].
Southern Evening *Echo* [SCL 1888-1908].
Southern (Daily) *Echo* (Bournemouth) 1888-1920+ [SCL;
Winchester Lib 1888-1908].
(Shirley & Freemantle) *Advocate* (Millbrook) 1894-
1920+.
S *Amusements* 1895-1912 [SCL].
S & Dist *Pictorial* 1912-20 [SCL].

Southsea *see Portsmouth*
Stockbridge *see Andover.*
Whitchurch *see Andover.*

WINCHESTER
Hants *Chronicle* 1772-1830 [SCL; West Sussex Record
Office, Chichester 1772-97, 1800-02].
W/Hants *Herald* (Basingstoke, Alresford, Alton, Bishop's
Waltham) 1869-79.
W/Hants *Observer* 1877-1920+ [Winchester Lib].
See also Southampton; Wilts: Salisbury.

WOOLSTON
W *Independent* 1905-11 [Southampton Central Lib].

ISLE OF WIGHT

Bonchurch *see Ventnor.*

COWES
IoW *Herald* 1868-71, 1889-1920+.
Beaven's *Advertiser* 1904-07.

FRESHWATER
F, Totland & Yarmouth *Advertiser* 1904-15.

NEWPORT
IoW *County Press* 1884-1920+ [Isle of Wight RO].

N *Times* 1898-1905 > IoW *Journal* 1905-20.

IoW *Leader* 1906-09.

Island *Star* 1910-20.

County Press Daily 1910-20+.

See also Shanklin.

RYDE
[NL = Lord Louis Library, Newport.]

IoW *Observer* 1852-1920+ [NL 1852-68, 1870-74, 1876-1882, 1884-1912, 1914-16, 1918-20+].

IoW *Mercury* 1855-60 > IoW *Examiner* 1860-61 [NL 1868-70, 1873-77, 1879-1900, 1914-20+].

IoW *Times* (Hants) 1862-1920+.

R *News* 1870-79.

R *Ventilator* 1871-74 [NL 1871-75].

R & IoW *News* 1880-1900.

See also Ventnor.

SANDOWN
IoW *Chronicle* 1866-1920+.

See also Shanklin, Ventnor.

SHANKLIN
IoW *Journal* (Newport) 1872-90.

S (& Sandown) *Weekly News* 1878-1919 > IoW *Guardian* 1919-20+.

S *Gazette* 1899-1920+.

Vectis 1896-1903.

See also Ventnor.

Totland see *Freshwater.*

Undercliffe see *Ventnor.*

VENTNOR
IoW *Advertiser* (Ryde, Undercliffe) 1869-72, 1884-1920+.

(V *Gazette* &) IoW *Mercury* (Bonchurch, Undercliffe) 1869-1920+.

V *Journal* (Undercliffe) 1870 > IoW *Express* (Sandown, Shanklin) 1870-1903.

Yarmouth see *Freshwater.*

For other newspapers covering Hants, see also Berks: Maidenhead, Reading; Dorset: Blandford, Wimborne; Soms: Yeovil; Surrey: Farnham; Wilts: Marlborough.

HEREFORDSHIRE

Early county newspapers – see Hereford.

[HL = Hereford Library.]

BROMYARD
B *News* (North Herefs, West Worcs) 1883-93.

B (News &) *Record* 1898-1920+.

HEREFORD [HL = Hereford Lib]
(Pugh's) H *Journal* 1770-1920+ [HL; Herefordshire Record Office 1770-1858].

H *Independent* (Ludlow, Glos, Worcs, Monm, South Wales) 1824-28 [HL].

H *Times* 1832-1920+ [HL 1881-1910].

H *County Press* 1837-40.

H *Weekly News* 1860-63.

H *Mercury* 1864-1920+.

H Weekly *Marvel* 1869-1904.

KINGTON
K *Gazette* (Rads) 1869-70, 1872-95, 1897-1907.

K *Reporter* (North Herefs) 1907-14.

K/North Herefs *Advertiser* 1907-18 > K *Times* 1918-20+ [Hereford Lib].

LEDBURY [LdL = Ledbury Lib]
L *Reporter* 1904-20+ [LdL].

L *Free Press* 1871-1908 > L *Guardian* 1908-21 [LdL].

See also Worcs: Malvern.

LEOMINSTER
L *News* (North West Herefs, Rads) 1883-1920+ [Leominster Lib 1888-1920+].

Rads *Echo* 1886-89.

North Herefs *Mail* 1898-99 [Hereford Lib 1897-99].

ROSS-ON-WYE
R *Gazette* (Newent, Mitcheldean) 1867-1920+ [HL].

Man of R (Forest of Dean) 1855-98.

For other newspapers covering Herefs, see also Glos: Lydney; Worcs: Tenbury Wells.

HERTFORDSHIRE

Early county newspapers – see Hertford; Bucks: Aylesbury; Hunts: Huntingdon.

[HA = Hertfordshire Archives & Local Studies, Hertford.]

BARNET
B *Gazette* (Chipping Barnet, East Barnet) 1856-89

B *Press* 1861-1920+ [HA 1875-1920*].

(Finchley *Telegraph* &) B (& Southgate) *Times* (Finchley) 1890-1907.

See also Middx: Enfield.

BERKHAMSTED
B *Times* (Tring, Chesham, Bucks, Beds) 1875-1900 > West Herts *Observer* 1900-02 [HA 1878, 1886-87, 1890-91, 1898].

B *Gazette* (Tring) 1904-20+ [HA 1894*, 1898*, 1910*].

See also Hemel Hempstead, Watford.

BISHOP'S STORTFORD [BSL = Bishops Stortford Lib]
BS/Herts & Essex *Observer* 1861-1920+ [BSL 1863, 1875-76, 1877-78, 1880-89; HA 1886-1920*].

East Herts & West Essex *News* 1889-99 > BS *Weekly News* 1899-1900.

Bushey see *Watford.*

Hertfordshire *continued*

CHESHUNT
Waltham Abbey & C (& Dists) Weekly *Telegraph* 1869-1920+ [Cheshunt Lib 1879-80; HA 1873, 1898].

Chipping Barnet see *Barnet.*
East Barnet see *Barnet.*
Elstree see *Middx: Edgware* .

HARPENDEN
H *Mail* (Redbourn, Wheathampsted) 1900-07.

HEMEL HEMPSTEAD
(Herts &) HH *Gazette* 1867-1920+ [HA 1883-1920+].
HH *Advertiser* (Berkhamsted, West Herts) 1895-1901.

HERTFORD
[HL = Hertford Lib; HM = Hertford Mus]
Herts (Huntingdon, Bedford, Cambridge & Isle of Ely) *Mercury* 1825-33 [HA 1825-30, 1832; HL 1825-28].
County Press for Herts, Beds, Bucks, etc. 1831-57 [HA 1831-38, 1851-52, 1854-55; HL 1845; HM 1831-33].
Reformer (Beds, Bucks, Essex, Cambs, Middx) 1834-43 > H *Mercury* 1844-1920+ [HA 1834-1920+; HL 1848-1867, 1907, 1909-12, 1914-15, 1919; HM 1834-37].
Herts *Guardian* 1852-1902 [HA 1852-96*].
H *Record* 1883-92 [HA 1883, 1886-88, 1890, 1919; HM 1919].
H & Ware *Chronicle* (East Herts) 1893-96 [HA 1893-1895].
Herts *News* 1907-10.
Herts *Record* 1919-20+.
See also Hunts: Huntingdon.

HITCHIN [HiM = Hitchin Museum]
H & Royston/Herts *Express* (Beds, Cambs, Letchworth, Stevenage) 1859-1920+ [HiM; Beds & Luton Archives 1867-68, 1886-1912*; HA 1859-70, 1877, 1882, 1886-1887, 1889, 1891, 1894, 1900, 1903-09, 1912-13, 1915, 1918, 1920].
Herts & Beds *Gazette* (Huntingdon, Cambridge, Bucks) 1861-65.
North Herts & South Beds *Journal* 1876-1913.
North Herts *Mail* 1906-19 [HiM 1913, 1915-16].

HODDESDON
H *Observer* 1894-1902.

LETCHWORTH
The *Citizen* 1906-20+.
(Garden City Co-Operators') *Record* 1912-17.
See also Hitchin.

Redbourn see *Harpenden.*
Rickmansworth see *Watford; Bucks: Chesham.*

ROYSTON
R *Crow* [HA 1855-65] 1876-77 > Herts & Cambs *Reporter* 1877-1920+ [Cambridge Central Lib 1876-1914; 1876-1920+; Royston Lib 1876-1920+].
R *Weekly News* 1889-1910.
See also Cambs: Cambridge.

ST. ALBANS [SAL = St Albans Lib]
SA *Times* 1855-65 > Herts *Advertiser* 1866-1920+ [HA 1855, 1858-1920+; SAL 1858-95, 1897-1920+].
Herts *Standard* 1877-1907 [HA 1877-1905*].
SA *Clock Tower* 1895-97 > SA *Gazette* 1899-1909.
SA *Post* 1906-09.
Herts *Post* 1910-13.
Herts *News* 1919-20+ [HA].

Stevenage see *Hitchin.*

TRING
T *Gazette* [HA 1894-96*, 1898*].
T *Telegraph* [HA 1876*, 1883*].
See also Berkhamsted, Watford.

Ware see *Hertford.*

WATFORD [WL = Watford Lib]
(West Herts &) W *Observer* (Berkhamsted, Tring, Chesham) 1863-1920+ [HA; WL].
W *Times* (Bushey, Rickmansworth) 1883-87.
West Herts/W *Post* 1887-1920.
W *Advertiser* 1889-92 [WL 1887-92].
W *Times* 1891-96.
Herts *Leader* (Bushey, Rickmansworth, West Herts) 1893-1916 [HA 1907; WL 1895-1900, 1913-15].
W *Leader* [WL 1893-97].
W *News Letter* 1907-20 [HA 1914; WL 1892-1916, 1919-20+].
W *Herald* (West Herts) 1908-11.
W *Illustrated* [WL 1914-16].
See also Middx: Harrow.

Wheathampsted see *Harpenden.*

For other newspapers covering Herts, see also Beds: Dunstable, Luton; Bucks: Amersham, Aylesbury; Lond: London.

HUNTINGDONSHIRE

Early county newspapers – see Huntingdon.

[CCL = Cambridge Central Library; HL = Huntingdon Library; NL = Norris Library & Museum, Huntingdon.]

HUNTINGDON
H (Northampton), Bedford & Cambridge *Weekly Journal* 1825-28.
H, Bedford (Cambridge) & Peterborough *Gazette* (Hertford) 1818-19, 1825-39 [CCL 1815-1920+; NL 1813-1816; Beds & Luton Archives 1815-37 > Cambridge *Independent Press*].
Hunts (County) *Guardian* (St. Neots, Huntingdon) 1870-1893 > Hunts *Post* 1893-1920+ [HL, index BMD 1885-1889, 1905-16; NL 1870-1919].
Hunts *County News* 1886-1920+ [HL; NL 1887-1909].
Hunts *Weekly News* 1889 > Hunts *Chronicle* (Cambs) 1889-1900 [CCL 1889-96, 1899-1900].
See also St. Ives; Beds: Bedford; Herts: Hitchin.

ST. IVES
SI & Hunts/Eastern Counties *Gazette* (Cambridge) 1857-1860 > Hunts *News* 1860-74.
SI *Chronicle* (Cambs) 1889-1901.

ST. NEOTS
(Illus) SN *Chronicle* 1853-55 [NL only], 1855-86.
SN Monthly *Advertiser* 1878-85.
(Hunts &) SN *Advertiser* (Beds) 1885-1920+ [NL 1885-1897, 1901-12, 1918-19].
SN *Free Press* 1898-1902.
See also St. Ives.

For other newspapers covering Hunts, see also Cambs: Cambridge; Herts: Hertford; Nhants: Kettering, Northampton.

KENT

The county included areas now in the LBs of Bexley and Bromley; and for the LBs of Greenwich and Lewisham, see under London, and map, p. 36

Early county newspapers – see Canterbury, Maidstone.

Abbey Wood *see Erith.*
Alfred *see Ashford.*
Anerley *see Penge; London: Lambeth.*

ASHFORD
A & Alfred *News* 1855-58 > Kentish *Express* (Hythe) 1858-1920+.
Kent (County) *Examiner* 1889-1913.
Tuesday *Express* 1903-20+.

BECKENHAM [BrL = Bromley Lib]
B *Journal* (Penge, Sydenham) 1876-1920+ [BrL].
B & Penge *Advertiser* 1888-1920+ [BrL].
B & Shortlands *Chronicle* 1902-13.
B & Dist *Times* 1905-20+ [BrL 1906-07].

Bellingham *see London: Lewisham.*
Belvedere *see Erith.*
Bexley *see Bexley Heath.*

BEXLEY HEATH [Bxl = Bexley Lib]
BH *Observer* (Dartford, Erith, Bexley) 1870-1920+ [BxL 1873-1920+].
BH, Bexley & Dist *Times* (Dartford) 1905-18 [BxL].
North Kent *Argus* 1920+.

Birchington *see Margate, Westgate-on-Sea.*
Blackheath *see London: Lewisham.*

BROADSTAIRS
B *Gazette* (St. Peter's, Isle of Thanet) 1881-89.
B & St. Peter's *Mail* (Thanet, East Kent) 1903-20+.
B & St. Peter's *Echo* (Thanet) 1907-20+.
See also Margate.

Brockley *see London: Lewisham.*

BROMLEY [Brl = Bromley Lib]
B *Record* 1858-1913 [BrL].
B (& West Kent) *Telegraph* (St. Mary Cray, Sevenoaks) 1868-1913 [BrL 1868-72, 1886-96, 1898-1913].
B *Journal* (West Kent) 1869-1912 [BrL 1869-85, 1887-1912].
B *Chronicle* 1891-1920+ [BrL 1891-96, 1898-1920+].
B & Dist *Times* 1899-1920+ [BrL 1888-1920+].
B *Local Guide* 1903-20+ [BrL].
West Kent Dist *Times* 1905-20+.
B *Mercury* 1919-20+ [BrL].
See also Essex: Stratford; London: Lewisham.

Brompton *see Chatham, Rochester.*

CANTERBURY [CL = Canterbury Lib]
Kentish (Weekly) *Post* pre1750-70 > C *Journal* 1770-88 > Kentish *Chronicle* 1788-1838 [CL pre1750-1828].
Kentish *Gazette* 1768-1920+ [CL; Univ of Kent at Canterbury 1768-1851; Canterbury Cathedral Archives 1823-70; Maidstone Lib 1768-1827].
Kent(ish) *Herald* (Rochester) 1802-03, 1824-1920+ [CL 1824-70].
Kentish *Observer* (Surrey, Sussex) 1832-1920+ [CL 1839-49].
C (Weekly) *Journal* 1836-1920.
C *News* 1855 > East Kent *Times* 1855-65.
Kentish *Chronicle* (Isle of Thanet, East Kent) 1859-1902.
Kent County *News* 1876-79 > Canterbury *Press* 1879-1891.
Examiner Advertisement/C *Register* 1895-1906.

CHATHAM [MA = Medway Archives, Rochester]
C (& Rochester) (& Gillingham) *News* 1859-1920+ [Chatham Lib, Gillingham Lib, MA].
C (& Rochester) (& Brompton/Gillingham) *Observer* 1870-1920+ [MA].
Kent Mercantile *Gazette* 1889-1920.
See also Maidstone, Rochester.

Cheriton *see Folkestone, Hythe, Sandgate.*

CHISLEHURST
C & Dist *Times* 1905-20+.
See also London: Lewisham.

Cliftonville *see Margate.*

CRAYFORD
C *Chronicle* 1919-20+.

DARTFORD
D *Chronicle* (Bexley, Erith) 1869-1920+ [Dartford Lib].
D *Express* (Greenhithe, Farningham, North Kent) 1875-1918 [Bexley Lib 1898-99].
(D &) West Kent *Advertiser* 1876-1920+
See also Bexley, Gravesend, Swanley.

DEAL
D, Walmer (Dover) & Sandwich/Kentish *Telegram* 1858-1918 [Dover Lib 1858-88].
D, Walmer & Sandwich *Mercury* 1865-1920+.

D *Chronicle*/South Eastern *Express* (Sandwich, Walmer, Dover, East Kent, St. Augustin's) 1875-1900.

D *Paper* (Walmer, Sandwich, East Kent) 1892-1920+.

See also Dover, Sandwich.

DOVER [DvL = Dover Lib]

Cinque Ports *Advertiser* [DvL 1825-27].

D *Telegraph* 1833-1920+ [DvL 1833-59, 1910, 1914-18].

D *Chronicle* 1835-1920+ [DvL 1840-41].

D *Express* 1858-1920+ [DvL].

D *Independent* 1860-65.

Cinque Ports *Pilot* (Margate, Ramsgate) 1860-67.

D *News* 1866-79 > South Coast *Echo* 1879.

D *Standard* 1871-1920+ [DvL 1910, 1914, 1919].

D *Times* 1887-90.

D *Observer* (Deal, Walmer, Sandwich) 1895-1905 [DvL 1896, 1898-99, 1902].

D *Times* (East Kent) 1905-14 [DvL 1905-07, 1910-14].

See also Deal, Dover.

EDENBRIDGE

E *Chronicle* 1905-20+.

ERITH [EL = Erith Lib]

E *Times* (Belvedere, Abbey Wood) 1883-1919 [Bexley Lib, EL].

E *Chronicle* (Belvedere) 1899-1918.

E *Observer* (Belvedere) 1907-20+ [Bexley Lib, EL].

See also Bexley.

Eynsford *see Swanley.*

Farningham *see Dartford.*

FAVERSHAM [FvL = Faversham Lib]

F *Mercury* (Sittingbourne, Whitstable, North-East Kent) 1860-1920+ [FvL 1879-82, 1897, 1907, 1912].

F/North East Kent *News* 1883-1920+ [FvL 1883-96, 1898-1906, 1908-11, 1913-20+].

F & North East Kent *Advertiser* 1903-10.

See also Sittingbourne.

FOLKESTONE [FkL = Folkestone Lib]

F *Chronicle* (Sandgate) 1855-1906 [FkL].

F *Observer* (Hythe, Sandgate) 1860-70 [FkL].

F *Express* (Sandgate, Shorncliffe, Hythe) 1868-1920+ [FkL 1868-97, 1899-1920+; HL 1917].

F *News* (East Kent, Dover, Hythe, Sandgate, Shorncilffe) 1876-90 [FkL 1884-86, 1890].

F *Advertiser* 1884-87.

F *Observer* (Shorncliffe, Hythe, Sandgate) 1884-95.

Holbein's/F *Visitors' List* 1884-99 > F, Hythe, Sandgate & Cheriton *Reporter* 1899 [FkL 1886-98].

F (Hythe, Sandgate & Cheriton) *Herald* 1891-1920+ [FkL].

F *Up-to-Date* 1893-1904 [FkL 1893-99].

F *Programme* 1895-1908 [FkL 1896-1905].

F *Telegraph* 1898-1901.

F *Daily News* 1905-14 [FkL].

See also Hythe.

Galley Hill *see Gravesend.*

Gillingham *see Chatham, Rochester.*

GRAVESEND [GvL = Gravesend Lib]

G & Milton *Journal* 1834-37 [GvL].

G *Free Press* (Dartford, North Kent, South Essex) 1855-1890.

G (& Dartford) *Reporter* (North Kent, South Essex) 1856-1920+ [GvL].

G *Journal* (Dartford, Northfleet, Galley Hill) 1864-92 [GvL 1864-83].

G & Dartford *Miscellany* 1871-90.

G *Argus* 1880-85 [GvL].

G & Northfleet *Standard* 1892-1915 [GvL].

N & Swanscombe *Standard* 1896-1915 [GvL].

Kent & Essex *Globe* 1898-1907 [GvL 1901-07].

See also Rochester; London: Greenwich.

Greenhithe *see Dartford.*

Greenwich *see under London*

HAWKHURST

Weald of Kent *News* (East Sussex) 1884-86.

Kent & Sussex *Post* 1886-1920+.

HERNE BAY [HBL = Herne Bay Lib]

HB *Press* 1883-1920+ [HBL].

HB *Argus* 1890-1905 [HBL 1891-1905].

HB *Advertiser* (Whitstable) > HB *Gazette* 1899-1902 [HBL 1899-1901].

See also Whitstable.

HYTHE

H & Sandgate *Echo* 1876-90.

H & Sandgate *Advertiser* (Shorncliffe, Folkestone) 1884-1920+.

H *Reporter* (Saltwood) 1890-1920+ [Folkestone Lib 1891-1919*; Hythe Lib 1896].

H & Sandgate *Standard* (Cheriton, Shorncliffe, Folkestone) 1902-06.

Cinque Ports *Chronicle* 1904-07.

See also Ashford, Folkestone.

MAIDSTONE [ML = Maidstone Lib]

M (& Kentish) *Journal* 1786-1911 [ML; indexed from 1843].

M/South-Eastern *Gazette* 1830-1920+ [ML 1819-1920+].

M *Telegraph* (Rochester, Chatham, Malling, West Kent) 1859-71 > Kent *Messenger* 1871-1920+.

Kent (& Sussex) *Times* 1875-1912.

(M &) Kent County *Standard* (Tunbridge Wells, Southborough, Tonbridge) 1875-1912 [ML 1875-96].

K *Messenger* (Dartford) 1881-1920+.

Sevenoaks *Telegraph* 1886-1900 > Kent *Messenger* 1900-20+.

Malling *see Maidstone.*

MARGATE [MgL = Margate Lib]

Thanet *Guardian* (Ramsgate) 1866-1920 [MgL 1866-76].

(Keble's) Margate & Ramsgate (& Isle of Thanet) *Gazette* (Broadstairs, St. Peter's, Birchington, Minster, East Kent) 1870-1920+ [MgL].

Kent: Margate *continued*

Thanet *Free Press* 1882-87 > Margate & Ramsgate/ Thanet *Chronicle* 1887-89.
Thanet *Times* (Cliftonville) 1896-1919 [MgL 1896-1905].
(Isle of) Thanet *Journal* 1904-09 [MgL 1903-04].
See also Dover.

Milton *see Gravesend; London: Greenwich.*
Minster *see Margate.*
New Cross *see London: Lewisham.*
Northfleet *see Gravesend.*
Orpington *see St. Mary Cray.*

PENGE
Anerley/P *Free Press* 1883-1920+.
P & Anerley (& Norwood) *News* 1908-20+.
See also Beckenham; London: Lambeth, Lewisham.

Penshurst *see Tonbridge.*
Plumstead *see London: Woolwich.*

RAMSGATE [RL = Ramsgate Lib]
Thanet *Advertiser* 1859-1920+ [RL 1869-83].
Pullen's Kent *Argus* (Isle of Thanet) 1873-1920+ [RL 1888-1920+].
Kent *Echo* 1878-85.
Kent *Weekly News* 1893-96.
Kent Coast/East Kent *Times* (Margate) 1866-1920+.
See also Dover, Margate.

ROCHESTER
[MA = Medway Archives, Rochester]
R (Chatham & Strood) *Gazette* 1830-68 [MA 1830-59].
R & Chatham (& Gillingham) *Journal* (Mid-Kent) 1857-1920+.
R & Chatham *Times* (Gravesend, Strood, Brompton, Gillingham) 1889-92.
R & Chatham (& Gillingham) *Standard* (Brompton, Strood) 1892-1908.
See also Canterbury, Chatham, Maidstone.

St. Augustin's *see Deal.*

ST. MARY CRAY
SMC, Orpington & Dist *Times* 1905-20+ [Bromley Lib, Orpington Lib].
SMC & Swanley *Express* (North Kent) 1900-15.
See also Bromley.

St. Peter's *see Broadstairs, Margate.*
Saltwood *see Hythe.*

SANDGATE
S (Hythe) & Shorncliffe *Herald* 1876-90.
S Visitors' *List* 1891-93 > S *Weekly News* (Shorncliffe, Cheriton) 1893-98 [Folkestone Lib 1891-97].
See also Folkestone, Hythe.

SANDWICH
S *Paper* (Deal, Walmer) 1893-94 > S *News* (East Kent) 1896-1900.
S *Advertiser* 1904-20+.
See also Deal, Dover.

SEVENOAKS
S *Express* 1863-1902.
S *Free Press* (Tonbridge) 1874-79.
S *Chronicle* (Westerham) 1881-1920+.
See also Bromley, Maidstone, Tonbridge.

SHEERNESS [ShL = Sheerness Lib]
S *Guardian* (East Kent) 1858-1920+ [ShL 1858-97, 1899-1920+.
S *Times* 1868-1920+ [ShL 1868-1915].
See also Sittingbourne.

Shorncliffe *see Folkestone, Hythe, Sandgate.*
Shortlands *see Beckenham.*

SIDCUP
S & Dist *Times* 1884-1920+ [Bexley Lib; Bexleyheath Lib 1886-1920+; Bromley Lib 1886-90, 1894-98, 1900-1920+].

SITTINGBOURNE
S (Faversham) & Sheerness/East Kent *Gazette* 1857-1920+ [Sittingbourne Lib].
North-East Kent *Times* 1900-20+.
See also Faversham.

Southborough *see Maidstone, Tonbridge, Tunbridge Wells.*
Strood *see Rochester.*

SWANLEY
S, Eynsford and Dist *Times* (Dartford) 1905-20+.
See also St. Mary Cray.

SWANSCOMBE
S *Chronicle* 1905-20+.
See also Gravesend.

Sydenham *see Beckenham; London: Lewisham.*
Tankerton *see Whitstable.*
Thanet (Isle of) *see Broadstairs, Canterbury, Margate, Ramsgate.*

TONBRIDGE [TL = Tonbridge/Malling Lib]
Kent *Times* (Sevenoaks) 1857-62.
T *Chronicle* (Southborough, Penshurst, Sevenoaks) 1863-60.
T *Telegraph* (Sevenoaks, Westerham) 1863-1905 [TL].
T *Free Press* (Mid Kent, South West Kent, Sevenoaks) 1871-1920+ [TL].
T & Sevenoaks *Standard* 1892-1912.
T *Gazette* (Southborough) 1909-17.
See also Maidstone, Sevenoaks, Tunbridge Wells.

TUNBRIDGE WELLS [TWL = Tunbridge Wells Lib]
TW/Counties *Gazette* 1855-1917 [TWL 1855-93].
TW *Journal* (Tonbridge) 1862-1904 [TWL].
TW *Weekly Express* 1863-1902.
TW *Standard* (Southborough, Tonbridge) 1866-1912.
Kent & Sussex *Courier* 1873-1920+ [TWL].
TW *Advertiser* (Sevenoaks, Tonbridge) 1882-1920+ [TWL 1914-18].
See also Maidstone.

Walmer *see Deal, Dover, Sandwich.*

Kent *continued*

WESTERHAM
W *Herald* 1882-1920+.
See also Sevenoaks, Tonbridge.

WESTGATE-ON-SEA
WS *Chronicle* (Birchington) 1882-89.

WHITSTABLE
W *Times* (Herne Bay, Tankerton) 1864-1920+ [Whitstable Lib; Herne Bay Lib 1879-81, 1885-87, 1889-90, 1892, 1899-1901, 1906-07, 1910-11].
See also Faversham, Herne Bay.

For other newspapers serving Kent, see also London: Greenwich; London (City of); Sussex: Lewes.

LANCASHIRE

Early county newspapers – see Blackburn, Bolton, Bury, Lancaster, Liverpool, Manchester, Preston, Rochdale.

[MCL = Manchester Central Library; NLW = National Library of Wales; TLS = Tameside Local Studies, Stalybridge.]

ACCRINGTON [AL = Accrington Library]
A *Guardian* 1861-63 [AL].
A *Times* 1868-91 [AL (indexed 1866-84)].
A (Div) *Gazette* (North East Lancs) 1881-1920+ [AL].
The *Echo* 1884-87 [AL].
A *Observer* 1887-1920+ [AL; Haslingden Lib 1907].
(Northern Morning News &) A (Weekly) *Advertiser* 1889-1915 [AL 1889-96, 1898-1905, 1911, 1914-15].
See also Blackburn.

ADLINGTON
A *Chronicle* 1889-1916.

Ainsdale, Altcar *see Formby, Southport.*

ASHTON-UNDER-LYNE
A(UL) (& Stalybridge) (Weekly) *Reporter* (Dukinfield, Hyde) 1858-93 [TLS 1855-1920+].
A *Standard* 1858-1900.
AUL *News* 1868-74 [TLS].
Evening Reporter 1876-1914 [TLS 1876, 1878-79, 1881-1902, 1904-14].
High Peak *Reporter* [New Mills Lib 1887-90, 1892-1901, 1903-20+].
AUL/Weekly *Herald* 1889-1920+ [MCL 1910; TLS 1887-1920+].
A Weekly *Sentinel* 1911-17 [TLS 1911-12].
See also Ches: Dukinfield.

Astley *see Leigh.*
Atherton *see Leigh, Tyldesley.*
Audenshaw *see Denton.*

BACUP
[BpL = Bacup Library; RwL = Rawtenstall Lib]
B & Rossendale *News* 1863-95 > Rossendale Div *Gazette* 1897-1901 [BpL 1863-97; RwL 1893-1901].

Lancashire: Bacup *continued*

B (& Rawtenstall) *Times* (Rossendale) Advertiser 1865-1920+ [BpL (indexed 1866-86, 1906); Haslingden Lib 1865-67].
Rossendale *Express* 1895-1917 [RwL 1914-16].
Rossendale *Echo* 1898-1920+ [RwL 1904-20+].
B *Chronicle* (Stacksteads) 1902-20+.
See also Haslingden.

Barnoldswick *see Colne.*
Barrowfield *see Colne .*

BARROW-IN-FURNESS
[BRO = Barrow Record Office]
B *Herald* (Furness) 1863-1914 [BRO 1868-1914].
B *Advertiser* 1868-70 [BRO].
B *Pilot* (Furness) 1871-77 [BRO 1876].
B (Furness & North Western) (Daily) *Times* 1871-85 [BRO 1871-84].
(The) *Vulcan* 1871-86 [BRO].
B *Evening Echo* 1894-98 [BRO 1879-80].
B *News* (Dalton) 1881-1920+ [BRO 1883-1920+].
B *Journal* [BRO 1896-1901].
North Western Daily *Mail* 1899-1920+ [BRO 1898-1920+].
Vickerstown *Chronicle* 1903-04 [BRO 1902-04].
B *Pioneer* [BRO 1905-08].
B *Guardian* 1912-20+ [BRO 1910-20+].

Birkdale *see Southport.*

BLACKBURN
[BbL = Blackburn Lib; BnL = Burnley Lib]
B *Mail* 1800-20, 1824, 1828-29 > B *Gazette* 1829-43 [BbL 1793-1828, 1832-39; BnL 1793-1829, 1832-39].
B *Alfred* 1832-35 [BbL 1832-34].
B/Weekly *Standard* (Darwen, North-East Lancs) 1835-1899 [BbL 1835, 1837-53, 1855-1904 (indexed 1837-1883); BnL 1841-52].
B *Mercury* (Clitheroe, Darwen, Burnley, North Lancs) 1843-46.
B (Weekly) *Times* 1855-1920+ [BbL 1855-59, 1861-1920+].
B *Patriot* 1859-73 [BbL 1870-73].
Northern Daily *Telegraph* 1886-1920+ [BbL].
B (Trade) (& Dist) *Advertiser* (North East Lancs) 1894-1911.
(B/Lancs) Evening/Daily *Express* 1887-98 [BbL].
B Labour *Journal* 1898-1907 [BbL].
B Weekly *Telegraph* 1899-1920+ [BbL].
B *Gazette* (Great Harwood) 1906-11 [BbL 1906-10].

BLACKPOOL [BkL = Blackpool Lib]
(B) (& Fleetwood) *Gazette* (Fylde) 1874-1919 [BkL 1873-1919 (indexed)].
B *Herald* (Fylde) 1874-1919 > B *Gazette* 1919-20+ [BkL 1876-1919].
B *Times* 1877-1920+ [BkL 1877-79, 1881, 1883-1920+].
(B & South Shore) *Weekly* (Standard) 1899-1917.
B *Journal* (Fleetwood) 1900-01, 1905.
(The) *Advertiser* 1909-16.
South Shore *Leader* 1915-18.

Lancashire *continued*

BOLTON
[BA = Bolton Archives; BoL = Bolton Lib]

B *Express* 1823-26 [BA, BoL 1823-26* (indexed 1823-1826)].

B *Chronicle* (South Lancs) 1825-1917 [BA 1825-26*, 1827-1917 (indexed 1825-35, 1845-71); BoL 1825*, 1827-1831, 1834-1917 (indexed 1825-35, 1845-71)].

B *Free Press* 1835-47 [BA, BoL 1835-47 (indexed 1835-1847)].

(Mackie's) B *Advertiser* 1848-49, 1874-1900 [BoL 1854-1859, 1868-74, 1875-92*].

B *Independent* 1859-60 > B (Evening) *Guardian* 1860-1893 [BA, BoL].

B *Evening News* 1868, 1889-1920+ [BoL 1867-1920+].

B (Weekly) *Journal* 1871-1920+ [BA, BoL (indexed 1871-97, 1901-20+)].

B Daily/Evening *Chronicle* 1873-1917 [BA 1873-83]

B *Express* 1888-99 [BoL 1888-96].

Teddy Ashton's *Journal* 1896-98 > (Teddy Ashton's) (Northern) *Weekly* 1898-1908 [BA].

BOOTLE
B *Times* 1878-1920+ [Crosby Lib 1881-1920+].

B *Herald* 1919-20+.

See also Liverpool.

Bradford *see Manchester.*

Brierfield *see Colne.*

Broughton *see Manchester.*

BURNLEY [BnL = Burnley Lib]

B *Advertiser* (East Lancs) 1853-80 [BnL 1852-80 (indexed 1852-63)].

B *Free Press* (East Lancs) 1863-64 > B *Gazette* 1864-1915 [BnL (indexed 1864-77, 1904, 1910-11)].

B *Express* (East Lancs, Clitheroe) 1877-1920+ [BnL (indexed 1878-1903, 1905-12)].

B & East Lancs Mid-Weekly *Gazette* 1884-87 [BnL 1884-88 (and card index)].

B *News* 1912-20+ [BnL (indexed 1913-20)].

See also Blackburn.

BURY [BuL = Bury Lib]

B (& Heywood) Advertising *Gazette* (Ramsbottom, Radcliffe, Elton) 1854-57 > (B) *Free Press* 1857-67 [BuL 1852-54].

B *Times* 1855-1920+ [BuL].

B *Guardian* 1857-1920+ [BuL 1876-1920+].

East Lancs *Echo* 1874-92 [BuL 1874-91*].

B Boro' *Advertiser* 1905-09.

B *Visitor* 1908-20+

B *Observer* 1909-12.

See also Bolton.

CADISHEAD
C & Irlam *Guardian* 1919-20+.

CARNFORTH
C (Weekly) *News* 1883-1920+.

Cartmel *see Grange.*

Castleton *see Heywood.*

Chadderton *see Middleton.*

Cheetham *see Manchester.*

CHORLEY [ChL = Chorley Lib]
C *Standard* 1864-1908 > Chorley (& Dist) *Weekly News* 1908-20+ [ChL 1865-84, 1880-1920+ (indexed)].

C *Guardian* (Leyland) 1871-1920+ [ChL (indexed)].

C *Weasel* [ChL 1881-83].

Clifton *see Swinton.*

CLITHEROE
C *Times* 1890-1920.

C *Advertiser* 1895-1920+.

See also Blackburn, Burnley, Nelson.

COLNE [CoL = Colne Lib]
C *Miscellany* [CoL 1854-57 (indexed)].

C & Nelson *Guardian* (Barrowfield, Brierfield) 1863-69 [Nelson Lib (indexed); CoL 1863-64, 1867-69].

C & Nelson *Pioneer* (East Lancs, West Yorks) 1882-90 [CoL].

C & Nelson *Times* 1884-1920+ [CoL 1875-1920+ (and printed index)].

C *Observer* (Barnoldswick) 1901-06 [CoL 1899-1903 (indexed)].

(The) *Bellman* [CoL 1908-17*].

See also Nelson.

Coniston *see also Westm: Windermere*

Cornholme *see Todmorden.*

CROSBY
Waterloo (& C) *Times* 1879-1920+.

Waterloo & C *Herald* (Formby, Seaforth) 1895-1920+ [Crosby Lib].

DALTON-IN-FURNESS
D *News* 1869-70, 1882-1920+ [Barrow RO 1883-92].

D *Guardian* 1912-20+.

See also Barrow in Furness, Ulverston.

DARWEN [DL = Darwen Lib]
D *News* 1876-1920+ [DL].

D *Post* 1885-99 > D (& County) *Gazette* 1900-20+ [DL].

D (Weekly) *Advertiser* 1893-1920+ [DL].

Monthly/Lancs *Leader* 1896-99.

See also Blackburn, Great Harwood.

DENTON
D & Haughton (& Dist) *Weekly News* 1873-75 [TLS 1873-78].

D (& Haughton) *Examiner* (Audenshaw, Hooley Hill, Dukinfield) 1873-92 [TLS 1876-92].

See also Ches: Hyde.

DROYLESDEN
D *Express* [TLS 1870-71].

D (Literary & Advertising) *Journal* [MCL, TLS 1854-55].

Earlestown *see Newton-le-Willows.*

Eastwood *see Cornholme.*

ECCLES
E *Advertiser* 1869-1908.

E & Patricroft *Journal* (Swinton, Pendlebury, Stretford) 1874-1920+ [Eccles Lib].

Elton *see Bury.*

Farington *see Leyland.*

FARNWORTH [FL = Farnworth Lib]
F *Observer* 1868-73 > F (Weekly) *Journal* 1873-1920+ [FL 1868-73*, 1883, 1889-92, 1894-1920+, index at Bolton Lib; Walkden Lib, Worsley 1915, 1919-20+].

F *Chronicle* 1906-17 [FL].

FLEETWOOD [FwL = Fleetwood Lib]
F *Chronicle* 1845-1920+ [Blackpool Lib 1845-73; FwL 1843-1920+ (indexed)].

F *Express* 1882-1920+ [FwL 1895-1920].

See also Blackpool.

FORMBY
F *Times* (Ainsdale, Altcar) 1894-1920+ [Formby Lib 1895-1920*; Southport Lib 1895-1918*].

F *Newspaper* 1897-1908 > West Lancs Coast *Chronicle* 1908-13.

See also Crosby.

Furness *see Barrow-in-Furness, Dalton-in-Furness, Ulverston.*

Fylde *see Blackpool, Lytham St. Anne's.*

Garston *see Liverpool.*

Gorton *see Manchester.*

GRANGE
G *Visitor* 1875-91 [Kendal Lib].

G & Cartmel *News* 1891-1920+.

G & Cartmel *Guardian* 1912-20+.

GREAT HARWOOD
GH *Post* 1894-99.

GH & Rishton *News* 1900-06 (Darwen) > GH *Gazette* 1907-10.

See also Blackburn.

HASLINGDEN [HaL = Hasingden Lib]
H & Rawtenstall *Express* [HaL 1864-66].

H *Chronicle* (Ramsbottom) 1867-71 [HaL].

(Bacup), H & Rossendale *Gazette* 1882-87.

H *Guardian* 1890-1920+ [HaL 1891-1920+ (indexed)].

H *Gazette* 1901-20+ [HaL].

Haughton *see Denton.*

Haydock *see Newton-le-Willows.*

HEYWOOD [HwL = Heywood Lib]
(Illus) H *Advertiser* 1855-1920+ [HwL ?1853-1920+].

H *Standard* (Castleton) 1878-82.

H *News* 1892-1920+ [HwL].

Hightown *see Manchester.*

Hooley Hill *see Denton.*

HORWICH [HoL = Horwich Lib]
H *Times* 1888 > H *Chronicle* 1888-1916 [HoL].

Hulme *see Manchester.*

Huyton *see Prescot.*

Irlam *see Cadishead.*

Kirkham *see Lytham St. Anne's.*

LANCASTER [LcL = Lancaster Lib]
L *Gazette* 1801-94 [LcL 1801-93 (part indexed); ?Harris Lib Preston 1816, 1818].

L *Herald* 1831-33 [LcL 1831-32].

L *Guardian* 1837-1920+ [LcL (indexed 1840-49, 1856-1861, 1870-80)].

L *Observer* (Morecambe) 1860-1920+ [LcL].

L *Times* [LcL 1892-97].

L *Standard* 1893-1909 [Lcl 1893-1907].

LEIGH [LLH = Leigh Local Hist Lib]
L *Chronicle* (Astley, Atherton) 1855-1920+ [LLH 1852-1920+].

L *Herald* [LLH 1859-69].

L (Tyldesley & Atherton) (Weekly) *Journal* 1874-1920+ [LLH].

L *Observer* 1886-99 [LLH].

L *Courier* [LLH 1904-06].

See also Tyldesley.

LEYLAND
L (Farington) *Weekly News* 1910-20+.

See also Chorley.

LIVERPOOL [LRO = Liverpool Record Office]
Gore's General *Advertiser* 1795, 1800-76 [LRO 1765-1864].

L *Chronicle* [LRO 1804-07].

L/Daily *Courier* 1808-1920+ [LRO].

L *Mercury* 1811-1904 [LRO; NLW; Leigh Local Hist Lib 1816-18; Wigan Local Hist Lib 1812-13*].

Billinge's L *Advertiser* 1821-28 > L *Times* 1829-56 [LRO].

Myers's Mercantile *Advertiser* 1822-1838 > L Mercantile *Gazette* 1839-75.

(L) Saturday's *Advertiser* 1823-33.

L (Commercial) *Chronicle* 1825-68.

(The) *Phenix* [LRO 1826-33].

(L Weekly) *Albion* 1827-87 [LRO].

L *Journal* 1830-84 [LRO; NLW 1837-84].

L *Standard* 1832-56.

L *Mail* 1836-81 [LRO].

L (Shipping) *Telegraph* 1836-99.

(Yr) *Amserau* 1843-59 [NLW 1843-59*; Univ of Wales Bangor 1844-59].

Northern/Daily *Times* 1853-61.

L *Herald* 1855-66, 1875.

L *Weekly Mercury* 1855-1916 [LRO; NLW 1839-1909].

(L) (Daily) *Post* 1855-1920+ [LRO; NLW 1904, 1906-1920+].

The *Porcupine* 1860-1915.

(L) Journal of *Commerce* 1861-1920+ [LRO 1914-85].

(Y) *Tyst* Cymreig 1869-70 [NLW 1867-70].

(L) *Weekly Courier* 1867-1920 [LRO; NLW 1908-20].

L *Leader* 1868-76.

Lancashire: Liverpool *continued*

L (Daily/Evening) *Albion* 1873-87 [LRO 1871-87].

Evening *Express* 1873-1920+ [LRO 1870-1920+].

The *Argus* 1876-80.

L *Lantern* 1878-82.

L *Weekly Post* 1878-1920+ [LRO; NLW 1897].

L *Echo* 1879-1920+ [LRO].

North End/L *Times* 1880-92.

(West Derby &) Wavertree *Times* 1881-92.

(L & Bootle) *Evening Times* 1883-94.

Halfpenny *Weekly* 1885-90 [LRO 1885-89].

L *Citizen* 1887-91.

L *Programme* 1888-89 > L *Reformer* 1889-92.

Garston & Woolton *Reporter* 1888-1920.

(Y) *Dinesydd* [Ruthin (Denbs) RO 1889-90*, 1895*].

(Y) *Cymro* / The *Welshman* 1890-1909 [NLW 1890-1907; Cardiff Central Lib 1890-1907; Carnarvon RO 1890-91, 1899-1904*; Ruthin RO 1890-96; Swansea Ref Lib 1891-97*; Univ of Wales Bangor 1891-1904].

Kemp's L/Lancs *Gazette* 1897-1920+.

(Y) *Brython* 1906-20+ [NLW, Univ of Wales Bangor; Cardiff Central Lib 1920+; Mold Lib, Swansea Ref Lib 1906-20+; Ruthin (Denbs) Record Office 1906-15].

Garston & Woolton *Weekly News* (South Liverpool) 1913-20+ [LRO].

Straight Talk 1915-19.

Walton *Times* (North Liverpool) 1919-20+.

See also Manchester, Southport.

Lonsdale *see Ulverston.*

LYTHAM ST. ANNE'S

L (& Kirkham) *Times* (Fylde, St. Anne's on the Sea, West Lancs) 1870-1920+.

(St. Anne's) *Visitor* (Kirkham) 1897-99, 1905-16.

St. Anne's (on the Sea) *Express* 1898-1920+ [St Anne's Lib 1904-20+].

L (St. Anne's) & Fylde *Standard* 1905-20+.

Makerfield *see Newton-le-Willows.*

MANCHESTER

[MCL = Manchester Central Lib; SL = Salford Lib]

(Whitworth's) M *Magazine* pre1750-60 [MCL, SL].

(Harrop's) M *Mercury* 1752-1830 [Bury Lib, MCL, Stockport Central Lib].

Anderton's Universal *Advertiser* [MCL 1762-89].

(Prescott's) M *Journal* 1771-81 [MCL 1772-81].

(Wheeler's) M *Chronicle* (Salford) 1787-1843 [MCL, SL 1781-1842; Harris Lib, Preston 1816, 1818-24 (indexed)].

(Cowdroy's) M *Gazette* 1801-29 [MCL 1796-1829].

Weekly *Despatch* [MCL 1804-38].

British *Volunteer* 1805-22 [MCL 1804-25].

M *Observer* 1818-20 [MCL 1818-21].

M *Guardian* 1821-1920+ (indexed from 1842) [Burnley Lib, MCL, Wigan Local Hist Lib; TLS: 1821-61].

M & Salford *Advertiser* 1831-48 [MCL 1825-48].

M *Courier* 1825-1916 [MCL].

Lancashire: Manchester *continued*

Aston's Exchange/M *Herald* 1827-36 [MCL 1792-93, 1809-26, 1834, 1836, 1843].

M *Times* (Salford) 1828-48 [MCL].

Britannia (Jones's Manchester, Liverpool & South British General) *Advertiser* 1834-38.

M *Examiner* 1846-55 > M *Weekly Times* 1855-1920+ [MCL].

M *Weekly Advertiser* 1853-61 [MCL 1854, 1857-60].

M *Daily Times* 1854-55 > M (Daily) *Examiner* 1857-1920+.

M *Weekly Guardian* 1860 > M *Weekly Express* 1860-1863.

M *City News* 1864-1920+ [MCL].

Free Lance 1866-80 [MCL].

M *Evening News* 1868-1920+ [MCL 1873-1920+].

Ben Brierley's *Journal* 1869-91.

M *Critic* 1871-78 > Reform *Gazette* 1878-79 [MCL].

M *Evening Mail* 1874-1915 [MCL 1876-1915].

Gorton, Openshaw & Bradford *Reporter* 1874-1920+ [MCL 1873-1918; TLS 1873-20+].

Comus/Momus 1877-82 [MCL].

Openshaw, Bradford & Gorton *Gazette* 1879-83.

Hulme *Gazette* 1879-83.

M *Weekly Post* 1879-87 [MCL 1875-87].

Northern *Advance* 1888-90 [MCL 1888-89].

Cotton Factory *Times* 1885-1920+ [MCL].

Sunday *Chronicle* 1885-1920+.

M *Citizen* 1888-93.

(South) M (Weekly) *Chronicle* 1889-1912 [MCL 1889-1897].

M (South) Dist *Advertiser* 1891-1920+.

(M) *Evening Chronicle* 1897-1920+ [MCL].

North M *Sentinel* 1800-1903.

Daily *Dispatch* 1900-20+.

Hightown, Broughton & Cheetham *Express* 1901-05.

Daily *Citizen* 1912-15.

M *Chronicle* 1917-20+.

See also Stretford.

MIDDLETON [MdL = Middleton Lib]

M (& Rochdale) *Albion* (Tonge, Chadderton) 1857-95 [MdL; MCL 1868-76].

M *Guardian* 1877-1920+ [MCL 1890-92; MdL 1889-1920+].

MORECAMBE [McL = Morecambe Lib]

M *Visitor* 1877-1920+ [McL 1898-1920+ (indexed)]

M *Times* 1881-1920+.

M *Guardian* 1920+.

See also Lancaster.

MOSSLEY

M & Saddleworth *Reporter* 1878-1920+ [TLS 1876-1920+].

M & Saddleworth *Herald* 1889-1901.

See also Saddleworth.

Lancashire continued

NELSON [NL = Nelson Lib]
N *Chronicle* (Colne, Clitheroe) 1890-1904 [NL 1890-1903 (indexed)].
N & Colne *Express* [NL 1891-1900 (indexed 1891-97)].
N *Leader* 1901-20+ [NL (part indexed)].
See also Colne.

NEWTON-LE-WILLOWS
(N &) Earlestown *Guardian* Advertiser 1880-1920+.
E & Newton *Examiner* 1882-1920+.
Makerfield *Examiner* (Earlestown, Haydock) 1895-1908.
Makerfield *Mercury* 1901-06.
Earlestown & N *Reporter* 1908-18.
Earlestown *Review* 1910-14.

OLDHAM [OL = Oldham Lib]
O *Advertiser* 1854-60 [MCL 1851-59, 1890; OL 1852, 1856-59].
O *Chronicle* 1854-1920+ [OL 1854-56, 1860-1920+; Royton Lib 1907-20+].
O *Observer* [MCL 1858, 1863].
O *Standard* 1859-1920+ [MCL; OL].
O *Times* 1860-63.
O (Evening) *Express* 1867-89 [MCL 1868-89; OL ?1867-1869].
O *Express* (Weekly ed.) 1880-89.
(O) *Evening Chronicle* 1880-1920+.
O Evening/Daily *Standard* 1880-1920+ [OL 1885-1920+].

Openshaw *see Manchester.*

ORMSKIRK
O *Advertiser* 1855-1920+ [Ormskirk Lib; Skelmersdale Lib 1857-1920+; Knowsley Lib, Huyton 1857-74].
O *Chronicle* 1872-74 (Skelmersdale, West Lancs) 1872-1878.
See also Southport.

PADIHAM
P *Advertiser* 1919-20+ [Padiham Lib 1918].

Patricroft see Eccles.
Pendlebury see Eccles, Swinton.
Pendleton see Salford, Swinton.

PRESCOT
(St. Helens &) P *Reporter* 1869-1920+ [Knowsley Lib, Huyton; St Helens Local Hist & Archives 1859-1920+].
P *Weekly Times* (Huyton, Rainhill, Whiston) 1907-16.
See also St. Helens.

PRESTON [PHL = Harris Lib Preston]
True British *Courant*/P *Journal* 1746 [PHL 1745-53*].
P *Review* [PHL 1793-94].
P *Journal* 1810 [PHL 1807-12].
P *Evening Mail* [PHL 1830-31].
P *Pilot* 1831-88 [PHL 1831-77 (indexed 1831-49)].
P *Chronicle* 1831-93 [Leyland Lib 1812-33; PHL 1812-1893 (indexed 1812-55)].
P *Observer* (North Lancs) 1837-40.

Lancashire: Preston continued

P *Guardian* 1844-1920+ [PHL 1844-73, 1875-1920+ (indexed)].
P *Herald* (North & East Lancs) 1855-1920+ [PHL].
Lancs Evening/Daily *Post* 1886-1920+ [PHL (indexed 1886-94, 1907)].
(The) *Clarion* [PHL 1891-97].
P *Monthly Circular* 1895-1915.
P *Argus* [PHL 1897-98, 1900-08].

RADCLIFFE [RdL = Radcliffe Lib]
R *Express* (Whitefield) 1883-1902 [RdL].
R *Guardian* (Whitefield) 1899, 1910-20+.
R *Times* 1899-1920+ [RdL; Bury Lib].
See also Bury.

Rainhill *see Prescot.*

RAMSBOTTOM
R *Observer* 1890-1920+ [Bury Lib 1892-97].
See also Bury, Haslingden.

RAWTENSTALL
Rossendale *Free Press* 1889-1920+ [Rawtenstall Lib 1883-1920+* (indexed 1887-1906)].
See also Bacup, Haslingden.

Rishton *see Great Harwood.*

ROCHDALE [RL = Rochdale Lib]
R *Observer* 1856-1920+ [RL].
R *Pilot* 1857-71 [RL 1863-71].
R *Spectator* 1860-68.
R *Times* 1871-1920+ [RL 1897-1920+].
R *Star* 1888-99 [MCL 1889-98; RL 1888-91, 1893-99].
R *Advertiser* 1902-03 > R *Free Press* 1903-04 [Haslingden Lib 1901-14].
See also Middleton.

Rossendale *see Bacup, Rawtenstall.*

SADDLEWORTH
S & Mossley *Standard* 1878-1900.
See also Mossley.

St. Anne's *see Lytham St. Anne's.*

ST. HELENS
[SHL = St Helens Local Hist & Archives Lib]
SH *Intelligencer* 1855-59 [SHL 1856-59].
SH *Weekly News* [SHL 1860-62].
(Dromgoole's) SH *Newspaper* 1869-1920+ [SHL 1862-1920+].
SH *Standard* 1869-77 [SHL 1865-77].
SH *Examiner* (Prescot) 1879-1920+.
SH *Lantern* [SHL 1887-93].
SH *Reporter* 1888-1920+ [SHL 1885-1920+].
SH *Free Press* 1907-11.
See also Liverpool, Prescot.

SALFORD [SL = Salford Lib]
S *Weekly News* 1859-89 [MCL; SL].
S *Chronicle* 1869-1916 [MCL 1873-1916; SL 1868-1910].

Lancashire: Salford *continued*

(Pendleton) (S) (& Broughton) *Reporter* (Weaste) 1880-1920+ [MCL 1879-81, 1886-1920+; SL 1879-1920+].
County *Telephone* 1889-93 [MCL 1889-92].
See also Manchester.

Seaforth *see Crosby.*
Skelmersdale *see Ormskirk.*

SOUTHPORT [SoL = Southport Lib]
S *Visitor* 1844-1920+ [SoL 1851-1920+].
S *Independent* (Ormskirk) 1861-72 > (Liverpool &) S (Daily) *News* (Birkdale) 1872-81.
S *Critic* 1878-82.
S *News* (West Lancs) 1881-85 > S *Standard* 1885-99 [SoL 1881-90].
S *Guardian* 1882-1920+ [SoL 1884-1920+].
S *Journal* 1904-20+.
S *Weekly News* (Birkdale, Ainsdale) 1905-08.

Stacksteads *see Bacup.*

STRETFORD
S Div/& Sale *Advertiser* 1891-1920+.
S Div *Chronicle* (South Manchester) 1889-95.
S *Telegraph* [Sale Lib 1904-14].
See also Eccles; Ches: Sale.

SWINTON
S & Pendlebury *Times* 1875-1901.
Pendlebury/S *Journal* (Pendleton, Clifton, Walkden, Worsley) 1877-1920+ [Swinton & Pendlebury Lib 1874-1920+].
See also Eccles.

TODMORDEN [TL = Todmorden Lib]
T (& Hebden Bridge) (Weekly) *Advertiser* 1862-1920+ [Halifax Central Lib 1862-69, 1871-96, 1898-1910, 1912-1920+; TL 1878-1920+].
T *Times* 1862-69 [Halifax Central Lib].
T & Dist *News* 1869-1920+ [Halifax Central Lib 1869-1882, 1884-95, 1898-1920+; TL 1879-1920+].
T *Herald* (Walsden, Cornholme, Eastwood) 1900-11 [Halifax Central Lib].

Tonge *see Middleton.*

TYLDESLEY
T *Weekly Journal* (Leigh, Atherton) 1873-1917.
T & Atherton *Chronicle* (South Lancs) 1878-1920+.
See also Leigh.

ULVERSTON [BRO = Barrow Record Office]
Soulby's U *Advertiser* (North Lonsdale) 1848-1914 [BRO].
U *News* 1883-1920+ [BRO 1886, 1891-94, 1896, 1900-1920+].
U/North Lonsdale *Mirror* (Furness) 1860-86 [BRO 1863-1885].
North Lonsdale *Herald* (Dalton) 1895-1910 [BRO].
U *Guardian* 1912-20+.

URMSTON
Western *Telegraph* 1898-1920+ [Sale Lib 1896-1909].

Vickerstown *see Barrow-in-Furness.*

WALKDEN
W *Advertiser* 1911-16.
See also Swinton.

Walsden *see Todmorden.*

WARRINGTON [WaL = Warrington Lib]
W *Guardian* 1853-1920+ [WaL (indexed 1853-66)].
W *Standard* 1858-62 [WaL 1858-62].
W *Advertiser* 1862-89 [Cheshire RO, WaL].
W *Examiner* (Mid Ches) 1869-1920+ [WaL 1875-1920+].
Mid-Ches *Examiner* 1870-78.
W *Evening Post* (Runcorn, Widnes) 1877-80 [WaL].
W *Observer* 1889-1914 [WaL 1885, 1888-1914].
(W) *Daily Guardian* 1891-1903.
W *Times* 1902-04 [WaL].
W *Review* 1904-20+ [WaL].

Waterloo *see Crosby.*
Wavertree *see Liverpool.*
Weaste *see Salford.*
West Derby *see Liverpool.*
Whiston *see Prescot.*
Whitefield *see Radcliffe.*

WIDNES
(W &) Runcorn *Chronicle* (Mid-Ches) 1902-20+ [Halton Lea Lib, Runcorn 1904-09].
W *Weekly News* 1878-1920+ [Widnes Lib].
W *Examiner* 1876-1920+.
W *Guardian* 1876-1920+.
See also Warrington; Ches: Runcorn.

WIGAN [WLH = Wigan Local Hist Lib]
W *Gazette* 1836-42 [St Helens Local Hist & Archives Lib; WLH 1836-41*].
W *Times* 1849-53 [WLH].
W *Examiner* 1853-1920+ [WLH].
W *Observer* 1855-1920+ [Wigan Archives, Leigh; WLH 1853-1920+].
The *Comet* 1889-94 [WLH].
W *Star* [WLH 1891-95].

Woolton *see Liverpool.*
Worsley *see Swinton.*

For other newspapers covering Lancs, see also Ches: Stockport; Yorks W.R.: Skipton.

LEICESTERSHIRE

Early county newspapers – see Leicester, Loughborough; Derbyshire, Nottinghamshire.

[LRO = Leics Record Office, Wigston Magna, Leicester.]

ASHBY-DE-LA-ZOUCH [AZL = Ashby Lib]
A(Z) *News* 1861-64 [AZL, LRO].
AZ *Gazette* 1876-88 [AZL, LRO].
See also Staffs: Burton-upon-Trent.

Leicestershire continued

Belvoir (Vale of) see Melton Mowbray.

CASTLE DONINGTON
CD (Weekly) **Express** 1858-59 > CD **Telegraph** (Derbys) 1860-67.

COALVILLE
C **Times** (Whitwick, Huddlescote, Ibstock) 1893-1920+ [Coalville Lib; LRO].
See also Staffs: Burton-upon-Trent.

HINCKLEY [HL = Hinckley Library]
H **Journal** (South Leics) 1859-62 [HL, LRO].
H **News** 1861-92 [HL, LRO].
H **Times** (Market Bosworth) 1889-1920+ [HL, LRO].
H **Free Press** (South West Leics) 1897-1900 [HL, LRO].
H **Echo** 1900-20+ [HL, LRO].
See also Warws: Nuneaton.

Huddlescote see Coalville.

Ibstock see Coalville.

LEICESTER
L (& Nottingham) **Journal** 1759-1920 [LRO; Bodleian Lib, Oxford 1771-1800*; Leicester University 1759-1853, 1855-74; Nottingham Lib 1758-88].
L **Herald** 1792-95 [LRO 1792-95*].
(Illus) L **Chronicle** 1792-1813, 1864-1920+ [LRO 1811-1920+].
Leics/L **Herald** 1827-42 [LRO].
Leics **Mercury** 1836-64 [LRO].
(Payne's) L (& Midland Counties) **Advertiser** 1842-1920+ [LRO].
L **Guardian** 1857-76 [LRO].
L **Express** 1861-64 [LRO].
L (Daily) **Mail** 1865-70 [LRO].
L **Evening News** 1872-78 [LRO].
L Daily **Post** 1872-1920+ [LRO].
L (Daily) **Mercury** 1874-1920+ [LRO].
Saturday **Herald** 1887-99 [LRO].
The **Wyvern**/L **Guardian** 1891-1906 [LRO].
L Daily **Express** 1892-95 [LRO].
L **Evening News** 1903-05 [LRO].
(L) **Pioneer** 1905-20+ [LRO].
L **Mail** 1910-20+ [LRO].
Kemp's Midland **Gazette** 1914-20+ [LRO].

LOUGHBOROUGH [LL = Loughborough Library]
L **Monitor** 1859-1920+ [LL, LRO].
L **News** 1861-70 [LL, LRO].
L **Advertiser** (South Notts, Sheepshead) 1868-84 [LL, LRO].
L **Herald** (North Leics) 1880-1920 [LL 1880-1919; LRO 1891-93, 1902-03].
L **Examiner** 1895-1903 [LL, LRO].
L **Times** 1908-15 [LL, LRO].
L **Echo** 1912-20+ [LL, LRO].

Lutterworth see Warws: Rugby.

Market Bosworth see Hinckley.

MARKET HARBOROUGH [MHL = Mkt Harbough Lib]
H **News** 1861-1864 [LRO].
MH **Advertiser** (Rutland, Nhants) 1869-1920+ [LRO 1854, 1869-1920+; MHL 1897-1920+].
Midland **Mail** 1898-1920+ [MHL 1898-1923].

MELTON MOWBRAY [MML = Melton Mowbray Lib]
MM **Times** (Vale of Belvior) 1887-1920+ [LRO, MML].
MM **Mercury** (Oakham, Uppingham) 1881-1915 [LRO, MML].
Melton **News** 1861-64 [LRO, MML].
See also Rutland: Oakham.

Sheepshed see Loughborough.

Whitwick see Coalville.

For other newspapers serving Leics, see also Derbys: Derby; Rutland: Oakham; Warws: Atherstone.

LINCOLNSHIRE

Early county newspapers – see Boston, Grimsby, Lincoln, Stamford; Notts; Yorks ER.

[GbL = Grimsby Lib; LCL = Lincoln Central Library.]

ALFORD
A, Spilsby & Horncastle **Gazette** 1899-1920+.
See also Horncastle, Skegness.

Axholme (Isle of) see Crowle, Epworth; Notts: Retford; Yorks W.R.: Thorne.

BARTON-UPON-HUMBER
North Lincs **Herald** 1854-58.

BOSTON [BL = Boston Lib]
B **Gazette** 1811-32 [GbL; BL 1811, 1814-15, 1829-32*].
B (Stamford), Lincoln & Louth (& Spalding)/Lincs **Herald** 1832-94 [BL, GbL 1832-35; LCL 1837].
B (Lincoln) & Louth/Lincs **Guardian** 1854-1920+ [BL 1854-70, 1873-1920+].
B **Gazette** (North Holland) 1860-93.
B **Independent** 1879-1912 [BL].
(B &) Lincs **Standard** 1912-20+ [BL].
See also Lincoln, Spalding.

BRIGG
(North) Lindsey/Lincs **Star** 1889-1920+.
See also Market Rasen.

Burgh see Skegness.

Caistor see Market Rasen.

Chapel see Skegness.

CROWLE
C **Advertiser** (Isle of Axholme & Marshland) 1871-1920+.
See also Epworth.

EPWORTH
E **Bells** (Crowle, Isle of Axholme) 1872-1920+.
Weekly **Herald** (Isle of Axholme) 1891-1913.

Lincolnshire continued

Frodingham see Scunthorpe.

GAINSBOROUGH
Yorks, Notts & Lincs *News* 1867-72.
G *Leader* 1897-1906.
See also Lincoln; Notts; (East) Retford.

GRANTHAM [GaL = Grantham Lib]
G *Journal* 1854-1920+ [GaL 1855-1901, 1909-20+].
G *Times* (South Lincs) 1884-1902.
G *Advertiser* 1902-06.

GRIMSBY [GbL = Grimsby Lib]
(Great) G *Gazette* 1853-58 [GbL].
G *Guardian* 1854-67 [GbL].
G *Free Press* 1860-68 [GbL].
G (Louth) (& North Lincs) (Independent) *Advertiser* 1854, 1858-87 [GbL 1858-87].
G *Herald* (North Lincs) 1863-81 [GbL 1863-67, 1876-81].
G *Gazette* 1866-1920.
G *Observer/Post* 1871-1904 [GbL 1871-94, 1896-1904].
G *News* 1874-1920+ [GbL 1875-1920+].
G *Express* 1878-91.
G (Weekly) *Express* 1883-98.
G *Independent* 1892-97.
Eastern/G Daily *Telegraph* 1897-1920+ [GbL].
G (& County) *Times* 1898-1916.
(G) Daily *News* 1910-15.
See also Lincoln; Yorks E.R.: Hull.

Holbeach see Spalding.
Holland see Boston.

HORNCASTLE
H *News* (South Lindsey) 1886-1920+.
H, Spilsby, Alford & Lincs *Standard* 1912-15.
See also Alford.

LINCOLN [LCL = Lincoln Central Lib]
L *Herald* 1829-32 [LCL 1828-32].
Lincs *Chronicle* 1833-1920+ [LCL, GbL 1833-37].
L (Boston) (Gainsborough) (& Newark) *Gazette* 1835-41.
L (& Lincs) *Standard* (Newark) 1836-48.
Lincs *Advertiser* 1846-50.
Lincs/L (Notts & North Midland) *Times* 1847-61.
L *Gazette* 1859-1920+.
L *Standard* (Grantham) 1862-69.
East Lincs *Gazette* 1866-70.
L *Journal* 1869-74.
L Daily *News* 1876-93 [LCL 1876-93].
Lincs *Echo* 1893-1920+.
L *Leader* 1896-1920+ [LCL].
L *Citizen* 1900-03.
L *Visitor* 1911-14.
See also Spalding, Stamford; Yorks E.R.: Hull; Yorks W.R.: Doncaster

Lindsey see Horncastle.
Long Sutton see Spalding.

LOUTH
L & North Lincs *Advertiser* 1859-1920+ [GbL; LCL 1859-1888].
L *Gazette* 1866-70.
L/Lincs (Halfpenny) *Echo* 1872-88.
L (& East/North Lincs) *Times* 1873-1911.
L *Herald* 1894-99.
See also Spalding.

Mablethorpe see Skegness.

MARKET RASEN
MR (Weekly) *Mail* (Brigg, Caistor, Lincoln 1856-1920+.

Marshland see Crowle.
Reepham see Norfk: Aylsham.
Rothwell see Nhants: Kettering.

SCUNTHORPE
S & Frodingham *Times* 1919-20+.

SKEGNESS
S (Spilsby, Alford, Wainfleet, Burgh, Chapel, East Lincs) *Herald* 1882-1916.
S, Mablethorpe & Alford *News* 1909-20+.

SLEAFORD
S *Gazette* 1858-1920+ [Sleaford Lib 1884-87, 1900-09].
S *Journal* 1884-1920+.

SPALDING
(Lincs, Boston &) S *Free Press* 1847-1920+
S *Guardian* (Holbeach, Long Sutton, Sutton Bridge) 1881-1920+.
S & Lincs *Standard* 1912-15.
See also Spalding.

Spilsby see Alford, Horncastle, Skegness.

STAMFORD
(Lincoln, Rutland &) S *Mercury* pre1750-1920+ [Boston Lib 1793-1900; GbL, LCL 1793-1920+; Lincs Archives 1793-1830, 1895-1910; Peterborough Lib 1800-55; Rutland Co Lib, Oakham 1895-1911, 1913-20; Sleaford Lib 1904-13].
Drakard's S *News* 1809-34.
(S) *Bee* 1830-33.
S (& Rutland) *Guardian* 1875-1916.
Rutland, Oundle & S *Post* 1885-95.
S & Dist/Rutland *News* (South Lincs, North Nhants) 1912-20+.
See also Boston.

Sutton Bridge see Spalding.
Wainfleet see Skegness.

WOODHALL SPA
WS *Visitors' List* 1899-1915.

For other newspapers covering Lincs, see also Notts: Retford; Yorks E.R.: Hull.

The **County of London**, 1889-1965, and surrounding counties

LONDON

The Metropolis poses a special problem in a Guide of this nature, with its 19th-century growth absorbing many individual places in the counties of Essex, Herts, Kent, Middlesex and Surrey, and later changes in administrative authority. The arrangement chosen is to include under 'London' all the places within the County of London created in 1889. Within this they are arranged alphabetically. The remaining areas which became part of Greater London in 1965 are listed under their historic counties.

[CWA = City of Westminster Archives.]

London, City of see under 'London', page 39.

Balham see Tooting; Surrey: Mitcham.

BATTERSEA [BL = Battersea Lib]
B & Chelsea **News** 1866-69.
South Lambeth, B & Wandsworth **Times** 1872-73 > B & Wandsworth **Observer** 1873-75.
Mid-Surrey **Gazette** (Putney, Wandsworth, Wimbledon, Roehampton, Barnes) 1878-1901 [BL 1890-1901].
B (& Clapham)/South-Western **Mercury** (Wandsworth) 1901-04.
B Boro' **News** 1906-20+.
See also Wandsworth.

Bayswater see Kensington, Paddington.
Bellingham see Lewisham.

BERMONDSEY
B & Rotherhithe **Advertiser** (Southwark) 1868-82 > Southwark (& B) **Recorder** (Rotherhithe, Newington, South Lond) 1882-1920+ [Southwark LS Lib].
See also Southwark.

BETHNAL GREEN
BG **Times** 1862-69.
See also Hackney, Shoreditch.

Blackheath see Greenwich, Lewisham.
Bloomsbury see Holborn, Westminster.
Bow see Essex: Stratford.
Brixton see Lambeth, Wandsworth.
Brockley see Lewisham.
Brompton see Chelsea.

CAMBERWELL
C & Peckham **Times** (Lambeth) 1870-74 > South Lond **Observer** 1874-1920+ [Southwark LS Lib].
C **News** (Peckham) 1876-80 > South Lond **Gazette** 1880-81.
C & Peckham (& Dulwich) **Express** 1871-75.
Peckham **Porcupine** 1892-97.
Peckham/South Lond Fiction/Popular **Press** 1893-96.
Searle's C, Peckham & Dulwich Artistic **Advertiser** 1907-16.
Dulwich **Post**/(Illus) South London **Mercury** 1901-16.

Camden Town see St. Pancras.
Canonbury see Islington.
Catford see Lewisham.
Charlton see Lewisham.

CHELSEA
West Middx **Advertiser**/C **Mail** 1856-1913.
C & Pimlico (& Brompton) **Advertiser** 1860-66.
Pimlico & C **News** 1865-69.
C **Times** 1872-75 [Chelsea Lib].
(Westminster &) C **News** 1879-85 > West Lond **Press** 1885-1920+ [Chelsea Lib 1865-1920+].
C **Courier** (Kensington) 1920+.
See also Battersea, Kensington.

Clapham see Battersea, Lambeth, Wandsworth.
Clerkenwell see Finsbury.
Deptford see Greenwich, Woolwich.
Dulwich see Camberwell, Lambeth.
Earlsfield see Wandsworth.
Eltham see Lewisham, Woolwich.

FINSBURY
Clerkenwell **News** 1855-71 > Lond Daily **Chronicle** 1871-72.
North Lond **Record** 1858-60 > C **Journal** 1860-69.
North Lond **News** 1860-95.
Clerkenwell **Dial** 1862-65.
C **Press** (St. Luke's, Holborn) 1877-86.
Clerkenwell **Chronicle** (St. Luke's, Holborn, North Lond) 1884-86 > (F) **Weekly News** 1886-1920+.
See also Holborn.

Finsbury Park see Middx: Hornsey.
Forest Hill see Lewisham.

FULHAM
[HFA = Hammersmith & Fulham Archives]
West Lond **Observer** 1855-1920+ [Kensington Lib 1855-88].
F **Chronicle** 1888-1920+ [HFA].
F & Walham Green **News** 1889-1904.
Fulham/West Lond **Observer** 1893-1920+ [HFA].
(West Lond &) F **Times** 1904-15.
F & West Kensington **Gazette** 1914-20+.
F **Gazette** 1919-20+.

GREENWICH
[GLH = Greenwich Local Hist Lib]
(G, Woolwich, Deptford &) West Kent **Guardian** (Gravesend, Milton) 1834-56.
G, Woolwich & Deptford **Gazette** 1834-38 > Kentish **Mercury** 1838-1920+ [Lewisham Lib; GLH 1834-1920+].
Kentish **Independent** 1843-1920+ [GLH].
Borough of G **Free Press** (Blackheath) 1855-65.
Orr's Kentish **Journal** 1860-66.
G & Deptford **Chronicle** 1869-85.
(Boro' of) G (& Deptford) **Observer** 1879-89 > Kentish **Mail** 1889-1909.
Deptford **Chronicle** 1895-98, 1907.
See also Woolwich.

HACKNEY [HAD = Hackney Archives Dept]
Eastern **Post** 1868-1920+ [HAD].
H & Kingsland **Gazette** (Shoreditch) 1869-1920+ [HAD].
(Borough) of H **Standard** (Bethnal Green, Shoreditch) 1877-1907.

London: Hackney *continued*

(Eastern) *Argus* (Bethnal Green) 1877-1912.

(H) *Mercury* (North Lond) 1885-1910 [HAD 1885-91, 1893-1910].

North Lond *Guardian* (Stoke Newington, South Hornsey) 1888-1916 [HAD].

North-Eastern *Leader* (Bethnal Green) 1892-96.

North Lond Fiction/Popular *Press* 1893-96.

H *Spectator* 1901-20+ [HAD 1910-11].

See also Shoreditch, Stoke Newington.

HAMMERSMITH

West Lond *Advertiser* (Kensington, Notting Hill, Paddington) 1860-66 [Hammersmith & Fulham Archives, index in prog., 1855-1920+; Kensington Lib 1855-88].

H (& Brentford) *Advertiser* 1861-66.

Suburban *Press* (West Lond) 1870-83.

West Lond *Advertiser* 1887-1906.

Shepherd's Bush & Hammersmith *Gazette* (West Lond) 1909-13.

H *Courier* 1920+.

See also Kensington.

HAMPSTEAD [CLS = Camden LS Lib, Holborn]

Kilburn *Times* 1869-1920+ [Brent Archives, Cricklewood 1870-1920+; CLS 1872-74, 1876-78, 1880-1887, 1893].

H & Highgate *Express* 1872-1920+ [CLS].

(South) H (St. John's Wood & Kilburn) *Advertiser* 1882-1920+ [CLS; CWA 1898, 1900-04, 1906-20+].

(Kilburn) *Post* (Paddington, Willesden, Hendon) 1886-1901.

H (& Highgate) *Record* 1889-1920+ [CLS].

See also St. Pancras.

Hatcham *see Lewisham.*

Herne Hill *see Lambeth.*

Highbury *see Islington.*

Highgate *see Hampstead, Islington, St. Pancras.*

Hither Green *see Lewisham.*

HOLBORN

News of the Week (Bloomsbury, Westminster, Marylebone) 1856-63 > *West End News* 1863-78.

(St. Pancras &) H (& Bloomsbury) *Journal* 1858-73.

North London *Advertiser* (Holloway) 1867-74.

H (& Finsbury) *Guardian* (Bloomsbury) 1875-1920+ [Camden Local Studies Lib 1893-94, 1899-1920+].

North-Western *Gazette* 1879-94.

See also Finsbury, St. Pancras.

Holloway *see Holborn, Islington.*

ISLINGTON [IL = Islington Lib]

I/Daily *Gazette* 1856-1920+ [IL 1856].

I *Times* (Finchley, Highgate, Hornsey, Holloway) 1857-1874.

(North Metropolitan &) Holloway *Press* 1872-1920+ [IL].

Canonbury & Highbury *Advertiser* 1875-88.

I *News* (Hornsey) 1877-1919.

Holloway *Advertiser* 1882-87.

London: Islington *continued*

(Northern) *Arrow* 1887-90.

Northern *Light* 1889-93.

(I) *Londoner* 1894-97.

I *Post* 1899-1908.

I *Guardian* (North Lond) 1914, 1919-20+.

See also Stoke Newington; Middx: Hornsey.

KENSINGTON [KL = Kensington Lib]

West Lond *Times* 1860-67 [Hammersmith & Fulham Archives].

Notting Hill & Bayswater *Times* 1860-70 [KL 1861-70].

K & Chelsea *News* 1865-69.

K *News* (West Lond) 1869-1920+ [KL 1876-1920+].

K & Hammersmith/West Lond *Reporter* (Notting Hill, Acton, Shepherds Bush) 1879-1906 [KL].

K *Express* (Notting Hill, West Lond) 1886-1920+.

K Weekly *Advertiser* 1888-90 > K *Society* 1890-96.

K *Post* (West Lond) 1918-20+.

K *Gazette* 1920+.

See also Chelsea, Fulham, Hammersmith, Paddington.

Kentish Town *see St. Pancras.*

Kilburn *see Hampstead; Middx: Willesden.*

Kingsland *see Hackney.*

LAMBETH [LA = Lambeth Archives, Minet Lib]

(The) *Ratepayer* (Southwark) 1850-53 [LA].

L/South Lond *Gazette* 1853-56 [LA 1853-54].

South Lond *Times*/L *Observer* 1856-65.

South Lond *Press* 1865-1920+ [LA; Battersea Lib; Southwark LS Lib].

Norwood *News* 1868-1920+ [Croydon Lib; LA 1868-1907].

Brixton & Clapham (& Streatham) *Post* (South Lond) 1871-75.

Norwood *Review* (Crystal Palace) 1880-1919 [LA].

South Lond *Gazette* 1881-87 > Brixton & Streatham (& Norwood) *Times* 1881-98 > Brixton & Streatham *Gazette* 1898-99.

Brixton *Free Press* 1882-1920+ [LA].

L *Post* (South Lond) 1883-91.

Brixton *News* 1886-91 > South London *Record* 1889-91.

N *Times* (Penge, Anerley, Crystal Palace) 1887-90.

Norwood *Press* (Dulwich) 1889-1920+ [LA].

(The) *Brixtonian*/(Brixton &/Borough of) L *Gazette* 1891-1915 [LA].

N Weekly *Herald* 1904-20+.

Norwood *Observer* (Herne Hill, Dulwich) 1905-17 [LA 1913].

See also Battersea, Camberwell, Southwark, St. Pancras, Westminster.

Lee *see Lewisham.*

LEWISHAM [LL = Lewisham Lib]

Sydenham *Times* 1862-83 [LL].

Sydenham, Norwood & Penge *Telegraph* 1872-75.

Sydenham (Forest Hill) & Penge *Gazette* (Crystal Palace) 1873-1920+ [Bromley Lib, LL].

(L & Blackheath &) West Kent *Courier* (Lee, Bromley, Charlton, Eltham, Chislehurst) 1880-87 [LL].

London: Lewisham *continued*

L & West Kent *News* (Lee, Eltham, Blackheath, Catford, Forest Hill, Norwood) 1881-85.

South-Eastern *Herald* 1882-1920+.

L *Opinion* (Lee) 1884-89 [LL 1884-85, 1888-89]

(Borough of) L *Gazette* 1885-1914 [LL].

Sydenham/Forest Hill & Crystal Palace *Times* 1886-1902.

Weekly *Advertiser* 1890 > L *Free Press* 1890-92 [LL].

Brockley *News* (Hatcham, New Cross) 1890-1920+.

Blackheath *Gazette* (Eltham, Lee) 1892-97.

Kentish *Press* 1893-96.

L & Lee *Herald* 1893-96 [LL].

West Kent *Argus* 1894-1920+ [LL].

Forest Hill & Sydenham (& Penge) *Examiner* 1895-1920+ [LL].

Lee *Journal* 1899-1920+ [LL].

L *Independent* (Catford, Lee, Blackheath) 1892-1900 > (L) Borough *News* 1900-02 [LL].

(Hither Green &) Catford *Journal* (Bellingham) 1901-20+ [LL].

L *Journal* 1902-20+.

Blackheath *Local Guide* 1912-20+ [LL].

LONDON (CITY OF) [GL = Guildhall Lib]

County Chronicle (Essex, Herts, Kent, Surrey, Middx) 1788-1902 [Herts Archives & Local Studies, Hertford 1809-25, 1818-32, 1870-71].

County Herald (Herts) 1818-73 [Herts Arch 1814-28*].

City *Press* 1857-1920+ [GL] .

Parochial *Critic* 1867-74 [Lambeth Archives].

(The) *Citizen* 1878-89 [GL 1878-1909].

(County &) City of L *Observer* 1908-15.

Maida Vale *see Middx: Willesden.*

Marylebone see *St Marylebone.*

New Cross *see Lewisham.*

Newington *see Bermondsey, Southwark*

Norwood *see Lambeth, Lewisham.*

Notting Hill *see Hammersmith, Kensington.*

PADDINGTON

(P, Kensington &) Bayswater *Chronicle* 1860-1920+ [CWA 1860-73, 1875-1920+].

P *Advertiser* 1861-66.

P *Times* 1870-1920+ [CWA 1870-78, 1885-1917].

P *Mercury* (West Lond) 1881-1920+.

P Weekly *Register* 1893-95 > Weston's/P *Gazette* 1095-1920+.

P *News* 1919-20+ [CWA].

See also Hammersmith, Hampstead, St. Marylebone.

Peckham *see Camberwell.*

Pimlico *see Chelsea, Westminster.*

Plumstead *see Woolwich.*

Poplar *see Stepney.*

Putney *see Wandsworth.*

Rotherhithe *see Bermondsey.*

St. George's *see Westminster.*

London *continued*

St. James's *see Westminster.*

St. John's Wood *see Hampstead, St. Marylebone.*

St. Luke's *see Finsbury.*

ST. MARYLEBONE

(Borough of) M *Mercury* (West Lond) 1857-1920+.

Borough of M *Newspaper* 1869-73.

(M) *Independent* 1885-92 > M *Times* 1892-1918 [CWA 1885-1911].

(The) *Advertiser* (St. John's Wood, Paddington) 1895-1909.

M *Record* (West Lond) 1914-20+ [CWA].

M *Chronicle* 1919-20+ [CWA 1919-20+].

See also Holborn, St. Pancras.

ST. PANCRAS [CLS = Camden Local Studies Lib]

SP *Reporter* (North London) 1857-69.

SP (& Holborn) *Times* 1858-61.

SP *News* (North London, Middlesex, Marylebone) 1859-1866.

United Albion *Circular*/SP *Gazette* (Camden & Kentish Towns, Hampstead, Highgate) 1866-1920+ [CLS].

North Londoner (Holborn) 1869-75 [CLS 1870-75].

SP *Guardian* (Camden & Kentish Towns) 1875-1920+ [CLS 1879-98].

North-Western *Telephone* (Kentish & Camden Towns, Hampstead) 1889-94.

People's *Advertiser* 1899-1900 > SP *Chronicle* 1900-1920+.

London/Whitefield's *Signal* 1905-20+.

SP *Record* (West London) 1920+.

See also Holborn.

Shepherd's Bush *see Hammersmith, Kensington.*

SHOREDITCH

S *Observer*/(Borough of) Hackney *Express* (Bethnal Green) 1857-1915 [Hackney Archives Dept].

S *Advertiser* 1860-69.

S *Mail* (North Lond) 1906-10.

See also Hackney.

Soho *see Westminster.*

SOUTHWARK [SL = Southwark LS Lib]

Lambeth & S *Advertiser* 1855 > South Lond *News* 1855-1861 [SL 1857-61].

South Lond (Local) *Journal* 1855-1902 [SL 1856-71].

South Lond *Chronicle* 1859-1907 [Lambeth Archives; SL 1859-92, 1895-1907]

S *Mercury* 1879-81 [SL 1879-91].

S *Standard* (South Lond) 1884-91.

(S & Newington) *Parish Parliament* 1888 > (West) S, Newington (& Bermondsey) Ratepayers' *Chronicle* 1889-92.

South Lond *Mail* 1888-1906 [SL].

See also Bermondsey, Lambeth.

Stamford *see Middx: Tottenham.*

London *continued*

STEPNEY
[THL = Tower Hamlets Lib, Bancroft Road]
East Lond *Observer* 1857-1920+ [THL].
Eastern *Times* (Tower Hamlets) 1859-64.
Tower Hamlets *Independent* 1866-84 > East Lond/Boroughs of Stepney & Poplar *Advertiser* 1885-1920+ [THL 1886-1920+].
Tower Hamlets *Express* (Poplar) 1869-76.
East End *News* 1869-1920+.
Courier (East Lond) 1874-79.
East Lond *Leader* (Tower Hamlets) 1882-86.
East Lond *Press* 1883-86.
Palace *Journal* 1887-93.
East Lond *Reporter* 1888-91.

STOKE NEWINGTON
(Hackney &) SN (& Islington) *Recorder* 1897-1920+ [Hackney Archives Dept 1909-20+].
See also Hackney; Middx: Tottenham.

Strand *see Westminster.*
Streatham *see Lambeth, Wandsworth; Surrey: Mitcham.*
Sydenham *see Lewisham.*
Tooting *see Wandsworth; Surrey: Mitcham.*
Tower Hamlets *see Stepney.*
Tulse Hill *see Wandsworth.*
Walham Green *see Fulham.*

WANDSWORTH
[LA = Lambeth Archives, Minet Lib]
Clapham *Gazette* 1854-55 [LA 1853-71].
South Lond *Courier* 1869-82.
Clapham *Observer* (Tooting, Balham) 1869-1920+ [LA].
W & Battersea District *Times* 1870-91 [Battersea Lib 1890-1905].
W & Putney *Observer* (Clapham) 1887-88 > W *Advertiser* 1888-1904.
Tooting, Balham, Wandsworth, Mitcham & Merton *Grumbler* 1889-1902.
South Western *Star* (Battersea) 1889-1920+ [LA 1890-1920+].
Streatham *News* (Tooting, Balham, Tulse Hill) 1891-20+ [LA; Bodleian Lib, Oxford 1891-1906].
South-Western *World* (Clapham) 1893-98.
Clapham Dist *Gazette* (North Surrey, Balham, Brixton) 1897-1900.
South-Western *Comet* 1898-1901.
W Borough *News* 1900-20+ [Wandsworth Lib 1884-1920+; Battersea Lib 1885-1920+].
(Streatham &) (Brixton) *Weekly Mail* 1903-08.
Balham (& Tooting) (& Clapham) *News* 1905-20+.
(Putney) *Newsletter* 1909-17.
Clapham Junction & Dist *Review* 1910-19.
Wimbledon Park & Southfields/Wandsworth *Newsletter* 1911-16.
Tooting & Balham *Gazette* (Earlsfield) 1919-20+.
See also Battersea.

WESTMINSTER
Lond *Chronicle* [CWA 1757-59, 1761-62].
W *Times* 1863-66.
W *Advertiser* 1866-69.
W (& Pimlico) *Chronicle* (West Middx) 1870-75.
(The) *Indicator* (West Lond) 1871-1920+.
West Central *News* (St. James's, Soho, Bloomsbury) 1877-81.
W & Lambeth *Gazette* 1881-91 [Lambeth Archives].
W *Times* (Pimlico, St. George's, Strand) 1885-96.
W & Pimlico *News* 1887-1920+ [CWA].
Lond *Argus* 1897-1907 [CWA 1897-1905].
(City of) W *Mail* (West Lond) 1900-18.
(The) *Westminster* 1902-06.
W *Express* 1904-16.
W *Record* (West Lond) 1916-20+.
W *Chronicle* 1919-20+.
See also Chelsea, Holborn.

Wimbledon *see under Surrey.*
Wimbledon Park *see Wandsworth.*

WOOLWICH
Jones's/Jackson's W *Journal* 1844-55, 1869-1901 [Greenwich Local History Lib 1844-66].
(Borough of) W *Gazette* (Greenwich, Deptford, Plumstead) 1869-1920+.
W *Herald* 1896-1920+.
Eltham & Dist *Times* 1905-20+ [Greenwich LH Lib].
See also Greenwich.

MIDDLESEX

Note: The inner London Boroughs which formed part of the County of London 1889-1965 are included under 'London'.

ACTON
A/Chiswick (& Turnham Green) *Gazette* 1871-1920+ [Ealing Central Lib 1873-1920+].
(A) (& Chiswick) *Express* 1900-18 [Ealing Lib].
(Acton) (& Chiswick) District *Post* 1911-20+.
West Lond *Post* 1913-20+.
See also London: Kensington.

Alexandra Park *see Hornsey.*
Bowes Park *see Enfield.*

BRENTFORD
(West) Middx *Mercury* 1871-93.
Hounslow/B *Independent* (West Lond) 1877-79.
B & Ealing/County of Middx *Independent* (Hounslow, Isleworth) 1883-1920+.
See also Hanwell; London: Hammersmith.

Brondesbury *see Willesden.*

CHISWICK
C *Times* 1895-1920+.
C *Express* 1902-05.
See also Acton.

Middlesex continued

Cricklewood see Willesden.
Crouch End see Hornsey.

EALING
Middx *County Times* 1866-1920+ [Ealing Central Lib].
West Middx *Standard* 1889-96.
E *Guardian* 1898-1900.
E *Gazette* (West Middx) 1898-1920+.
See also Brentford.

EDGWARE
E Reporter, Stanmore & Elstree *Chronicle* 1890-94.

EDMONTON
E & Tottenham Weekly *Guardian* 1884-1906.
See also Enfield, Tottenham.

ENFIELD
Meyer's/E *Observer* 1874-1913 > E *Gazette* 1913-20+ [Enfield Local Hist Lib, Southgate Town Hall 1859-1920+].
E (& Edmonton) *Chronicle* (Barnet) 1898-1904 [Enfield LH Lib 1898-1903].
Middx *Gazette* 1889-1913.
Bowes Park *Weekly News* 1904-20+.

FINCHLEY
(F) (Free) *Press* 1895-1920+.
F *Guardian* 1902-05.
F *Mail* (Golders Green, Hendon) 1912-15.
See also Hendon; Herts: Barnet; London: Islington.

Friern Barnet see Hornsey, Southgate.
Golders Green see Finchley.

HANWELL
H *Gazette* (Brentford) 1898-1920+ [Ealing Lib].

HARROW
H (Monthly) *Gazette* 1855-1920+.
H (& Wealdstone) *Press* (Watford) 1892-97.
(Wealdstone) H (& Wembley) *Observer* (Pinner) 1895-1920+ [Brent Archives, Cricklewood 1895-98, 1906-1920+].
H & Wealdstone *News* 1907-10.
Wembley & Dist *Recorder* 1911-15.
See also Uxbridge.

HENDON
H (& Finchley) *Times* (Hampstead) 1876-1920+.
(H/Middx) *Courier* 1887-97.
H *Advertiser* 1894-1920+.
See also Finchley; London: Hampstead.

HORNSEY
North Middx *Chronicle* 1869-1920+ [Islington Lib 1884-1890, 1908-1914].
Seven Sisters/H (& Finsbury Park) *Journal* (North Islington, Muswell Hill) 1879-1920+.
North Lond *Mercury* (Crouch End) 1899-1905.
Muswell Hill *Record* (Alexandra Park, Friern Barnet) 1908-20+.
See also Tottenham; London: Hackney, Islington.

HOUNSLOW
(County of) Middx *Chronicle* (Staines) 1860-1920+ [Hounslow Lib 1871-1920+].
See also Brentford.

Isleworth see Brentford.
Northwood see Ruislip, Uxbridge.
Palmers Green see Southgate.

PINNER
P *Gazette* 1895-99.
See also Harrow.

QUEEN'S PARK
(QP) *Advertiser* (West London) 1889-1920+.

RUISLIP
R-Northwood *Courier* (Uxbridge) 1908-20+ [Uxbridge Lib 1908-18, 1920+].
See also Uxbridge.

SOUTHALL
S *News* 1885-88 [Ealing Central Lib].
S-Norwood *Gazette* 1894-1920+ [Ealing Central Lib; Uxbridge Lib 1902, 1905, 1909, 1911-12].
See also Staines.

SOUTHGATE
(North Middx &) S *Messenger* 1856-62.
(S & Friern Barnet) *Sentinel* (Wood Green) 1895-1920+ [Enfield Lib 1895-96].
Recorder (Palmers Green, Winchmore Hill, Southgate) 1907-16.
Palmers Green & S *Gazette* [Enfield Lib 1915-16, 1920+].
See also Tottenham.

STAINES
West Middx *Herald* 1855-95.
Middx & Surrey *Express* (Southall) 1895-1909.
West Middx *Times* (Egham) Courier 1898-1920+.
See also Hounslow; Surrey: Egham.

Stamford Hill see Tottenham.

STANMORE
S *Observer* 1895-1900.
See also Edgware.

TOTTENHAM
(T & Edmonton/Coventry's) (Weekly) *Advertiser* 1855-83 [Enfield Lib 1861-83].
T & Edmonton *Weekly Herald* (Southgate, North Middx, West Essex) 1869-1920+ [Enfield Lib]
T *Observer* (Wood Green, North Lond) 1875-79.
North Lond *Echo* (Edmonton, Hornsey, Wood Green, Southgate) 1886-1901.
T & Stamford Hill *Times* (Stoke Newington) 1890-1904.
T & Wood Green *Star* 1891-96 > Middx *Mail* 1896.
Saltmarsh's *Local Notes* (Edmonton, Stamford Hill, Wood Green) 1893-95 > North Middx (Weekly) *Standard* 1895-1901.
See also Edmonton.

Turnham Green see Acton.

Middlesex *continued*

UXBRIDGE [UL = Uxbridge Lib]

U *Times* (West Middx) 1869-72.

(Broadwater's) (Middx &) Bucks *Advertiser* (Harrow, Ruislip, Northwood, South Bucks) 1861-1920+ [Ealing Lib 1861-74; UL 1861, 1869, 1871-73, 1874-1920+].

(U) *Marvel* 1873-77.

U *Gazette* (Bucks) 1882-1917 [UL 1893, 1903-17].

U *Review* 1899-1906 [UL 1899-1905].

See also Ruislip; Bucks: Amersham.

Wealdstone *see Harrow.*

Wembley *see Harrow.*

WILLESDEN

W (& Kilburn) *Chronicle* 1877-1920+ [Brent Archives].

W *Herald* (Kilburn) 1884-93 > W *Times* 1893-94.

Brondesbury, Cricklewood & W Green *Advertiser* 1892-1895 > Maida Vale & Brondesbury *Free Press* 1895.

W *Citizen* 1903-20+.

W *Call* 1913-18.

See also London: Hampstead.

Winchmore Hill *see Southgate.*

Wood Green *see Southgate, Tottenham.*

For other newspapers covering Middx, see also Bucks: Amersham; Hants: Basingstoke; Herts: Hertford; London: London (City of), St. Pancras; Surrey: Chertsey.

Monmouthshire (Gwent), see Wales – page 70

NORFOLK

Early county newspapers – see Norwich; Suff: Bury.

[NSL = Norfolk Studies Library, Norwich.]

Attleborough *see Thetford.*

AYLSHAM

A & Reepham (& Foulsham) *Post* 1919-20+.

Brandon *see Thetford.*

CROMER

C & North Walsham/North Norfk *Post* 1890-1920.

C, Sheringham & Dist *Weekly Press* 1913-20+.

Dereham *see East Dereham.*

DISS

D *Express* 1866-1920+ [NSL].

D, Harleston, Bungay (Beccles) & Eye *Journal* 1910-1920+.

DOWNHAM MARKET

DM *Gazette* 1879-1920+.

DM *News* (Wimbotsham, Stoke Ferry) 1903-15.

EAST DEREHAM

Norfk *Herald* 1856-65.

Norfk *Free Press* 1878-90.

D & Fakenham *Times* 1880-1920+.

Norfolk *continued*

Eye *see Diss.*

FAKENHAM

F *Post* 1919-20+.

See also East Dereham.

Foulsham *see Aylsham.*

GREAT YARMOUTH

Y/Lowestoft *Free Press* 1853-57 > Y *Independent* 1857-1920+.

Y *Chronicle* (East Norfk, Suffk) 1863-91.

Y/North Norfk *Constitutionalist* 1869-73 > Y *Gazette* (Gorleston) 1873-95 > Y *Advertiser* 1898-1901.

Y & Gorleston *Times* 1880-1920+.

Y *Mercury* (Gorleston, North Norfk) 1880-1920+.

Y (& East Norfk) (Weekly) *Standard* (East Norfk, North Walsham, Gorleston) 1906-16.

See also Norwich; Suffk: Bury St. Edmunds, Lowestoft.

Harleston *see Diss.*

Harling *see Thetford.*

HOLT

H, Melton Constable & Wells Post 1919-20+.

HUNSTANTON

H *Telephone* (West Norfk) 1878-85, 1892 > H *Herald* (Lynn Regis) 1892-93.

H *News* 1903-13.

(KING'S) LYNN [LL = Lynn Lib]

L *Advertiser* (West Norfk, Wisbech, Cambs) 1842-1920+ [LL]. Indexes to Mges and Obits published.

L *Record* (West Norfk) 1866-70.

L *News* (Cambs) 1868-1920+ [LL 1866-1920+].

(K)L (Weekly) *Journal* 1870-90.

L *Opinion* 1909-12.

See also Norwich; Cambs: Wisbech.

Lynn (Regis) *see Hunstanton, King's Lynn.*

NORTH WALSHAM

NW *Post* (East Norfolk) 1919-20+.

See also Cromer, Great Yarmouth.

NORWICH

N *Mercury* pre1750-1920+ [NSL].

Norfk *Chronicle*, 1776-1920+ [NSL; Bodleian Lib, Oxford 1828-76*].

N, Yarmouth & Lynn *Courier* 1818-23.

(The) *East Anglian* (Suffk, Cambs, Lynn, Yarmouth) 1830-33.

Norfk & N *Monitor* 1840-45.

Norfk *News* 1845-1920+ [NSL 1845-83].

Norfk/N *Advertiser* 1860-63.

(N) *Argus* 1863-93 > Norfk Weekly *Standard* 1893-1913.

People's Weekly *Journal* (Suffk, Cambs) 1864-1920+.

Eastern (Weekly) *Express* 1867-71 > Eastern *Weekly Press* 1871-1918.

Eastern (Counties) *Daily Press* 1870-1920+ [NSL].

Norfk *Mail* (Yarmouth, Lowestoft) 1876-86.

(Eastern) *Evening News* 1882-1920+.

Norfk *Weekly Standard* 1887-93.

Norfk Daily/Evening *Standard* 1887-1905.

Norfk *News* (Lowestoft ed.) 1919-20+.

See also Suffk: Bury St. Edmunds.

Sheringham *see Cromer.*

Stoke Ferry *see Downham Market.*

SWAFFHAM

S *Journal* 1876-90.

See also Thetford.

THETFORD

T & Watton *Times* 1880-1920+.

T (& Watton) (Weekly) *Post* (Attleborough, Brandon, Harling) 1905-06 > T & Watton (Weekly) *Standard* (Attleborough, Harling, Swaffham) 1908-16.

Watton *see Thetford.*

WELLS

W *Herald* 1888-92.

Wimbotsham *see Downham Market.*

Yarmouth *see Great Yarmouth.*

NORTHAMPTONSHIRE

Early county newspapers – see Northampton; Hunts: Huntingdon.

[NRO = Northants Record Office, Northampton.]

BRACKLEY

B *Observer* (Bucks, Oxon, Bicester) 1869-1901.

See also Bucks: Buckingham; Oxon: Bicester.

DAVENTRY

D *Spectator* 1869-76.

D *Express* 1869-1920+.

Desborough *see Kettering.*

Higham Ferrers, Irthlingborough *see Rushden.*

KETTERING [KL = Kettering Library]

(South) Midland *Free Press* 1858-1917 [Leics RO, Wigston Magna, Leicester; Loughborough Lib 1886].

K *Observer* (Rothwell, Desborough, North Nhants) 1882-90.

K *Guardian* (North Nhants) 1882-1920+ [KL].

K *Leader* 1890-1901 [KL].

(Nhants) Evening *Telegraph* 1898-1920+.

Nhants & Hunts *Gazette* 1913-20+.

NORTHAMPTON [NL = Northampton Lib]

N *Mercury* pre1750-1920+ [NRO; NL; Bedford Central Lib 1851-1900; Banbury Lib, Oxford Central Lib pre1750-1850; Beds & Luton Archives 1825-36; Bodleian Lib, Oxford 1800-14, 1818-32].

County Press (Beds, Bucks, Hunts) 1808-11.

N (& Leamington/Wellingborough) *Free Press* 1831-34.

N *Herald* 1831-1920+ [NL, NRO; Bodleian Lib, Oxford 1831-56].

N *Express* 1860-04.

Nhants *Guardian* (North Bucks) 1876-90 [NL 1876-90].

N Weekly *Reporter* 1881-85 [NL 1881-84].

N Daily *Chronicle* 1881-1920+ [NRO 1880-1920+; NL 1901-20+].

N/Nhants *Nonconformist* 1889-1910.

N *Independent* 1905-20+ [NL].

See also Hunts: Huntingdon.

Oundle *see Lincs: Stamford.*

PETERBOROUGH [PL = Peterborough Lib]

P (Weekly News &) *Advertiser* 1854-1920+ [PL].

P *Times* 1865-74 [PL].

P & Hunts *Standard* 1872-1920+ [PL].

P *Express* 1884-1917.

P *Evening News* 1896, 1899-1911.

(P) *Citizen* 1903-20+ [PL 1898-1920+].

Saturday *Citizen* 1909-12.

See also Hunts: Huntingdon.

Raunds *see Irthlingborough.*

Rockingham *see Yorks E..R.: Hull*

Rothwell *see Kettering*

RUSHDEN

R *Echo* (Higham Ferrers, Irthlingborough, Raunds) 1897-1920+.

Towcester *see Bucks: Wolverton.*

WELLINGBOROUGH

W (& Kettering) *News* 1877-1920+.

W *Post* 1886-1920+.

See also Northampton.

For other newspapers covering Northants, see also Leics: Market Harborough; Lincs: Stamford; Oxon: Banbury.

NORTHUMBERLAND

Early county newspapers – see Berwick, Newcastle.

[DUL = Durham University Library; GL = Gateshead Lib, NCL = Newcastle City Library; NRO = Nhumbd Record Office, North Gosforth, Newcastle-upon-Tyne; NTL = North Tyneside Library, North Shields; NU = Newcastle University.]

ALNWICK

A *Mercury* 1854-83 [NCL 1860-64; NRO 1859-85; NU 1854-59].

A *Journal* & Domestic Miscellany 1859-79 [NCL 1859-1882; NRO 1862-75, 1878; NU 1860-82; Durham University Lib 1859-82].

A & County *Gazette* 1883-1920+ [NRO 1883-97, 1899-1913, 1920+].

A *Guardian* 1886-1920+.

Northumberland *continued*

BERWICK-UPON-TWEED

[BL = Berwick Lib; BRO = Berwick Record Office]

(British Gazette &) B *Advertiser* 1808-1920+ [BL 1838, 1901-13, 1916-20+; BRO 1808-1907, 1911-13, 1917-1918; NRO 1808-29, 1831-33, 1835-37, 1839-61, 1863-70, 1872, 1874-85, 1887-93, 1898, 1901-04, 1906-1907, 1911-13, 1917-18].

B (& Kelso) *Warder* 1835-84 > Border Counties *Gazette* & Agriculturist 1884-98 [BRO 1838-40].

Berwickshire *News* 1869-1920+.

Berwickshire *Gazette* 1885-95.

B *Mercury* 1901-20+.

(Illus) B *Journal* 1855-1920+ [BL 1855-1910, 1912-1920+; NRO 1865, 1881, 1903, 1906, 1915].

BLYTH

B (Illus) (Bi-)(Weekly) *News* 1874-1920+ [Blyth Lib, NRO 1878-97; Morpeth Lib 1878-94].

B *Examiner* 1888-94 [Blyth Lib 1883-93].

HALTWHISTLE

H & Alston *News* (Brampton) 1892-95.

H *Echo* 1904-20+.

HEXHAM

H *Courant* 1864-1920+ [NRO].

H *Herald* 1868-1920+ [NRO 1868-99, 1904-20+].

H *Weekly News* 1904-20+.

MORPETH

M (Monthly) *Herald* 1854-1920+ [NRO 1854-1900, 1910-1920].

NEWCASTLE-UPON-TYNE

N *Gazette* pre1750-52 [DUL, NCL].

N *Journal* pre1750-88 [DUL, NCL ; GL pre1750-82].

N (Weekly) *Courant* pre1750-1902 > N Weekly *Journal* 1902-10 [DUL pre-1750-1800; GL pre1750-1830; NCL pre1750-1908; NRO 1828-29; NTL 1802, 1816-27].

N *Intelligencer* 1755-59 [NCL].

N (Weekly) *Chronicle* 1764-1920+ [Darlington Lib 1782, 1789; DUL 1764-1800; NCL 1764-1920+; GL 1764-1820].

N *Advertiser* 1788-1814 [DUL, NCL; GL 1789-99].

Tyne *Mercury* (Durham, Cumbd) 1802-46 [NCL; DUL 1802-28; GL 1805-27; NTL 1811-27].

Northern *Free Press* [NCL 1832, 1837-40].

N (Daily) *Journal* 1832-1920+ [NCL].

Northern *Liberator* 1837-40 [NCL].

Great Northern/N *Advertiser* 1840-48.

N *Guardian* 1846-72 [NCL].

North of England *Advertiser* 1855-84.

Northern *Daily Express* 1855-86.

(N) *Daily Chronicle* 1858-1920+ [NCL].

N *Weekly Express* 1865-86.

N *Evening Express* 1868-86.

North of England *Farmer* 1870-76 [NCL 1870-75].

N Evening/Daily *Courant* 1870-76 [NCL].

Tyneside Daily *Echo* (North Durham) 1880-88 [GL].

The *Northumbrian* 1881-86.

Northumberland: Newcastle *continued*

Northern (Weekly) *Leader* 1884-1919 [NCL 1886-91].

N Daily *Leader* 1885-1903 [NCL].

Evening *Chronicle* 1885-1920+ [NCL 1885-1920+].

N Evening/Daily *News* 1893-99 [NCL].

Northern *Gossip* 1895-1908.

Evening *Leader* 1899-1903 > Evening *Mail* 1903-05.

North *Mail* 1901-20+ [NCL 1914, 1917, 1919-20+].

Northern *Athlete* 1906-11.

Northern *Democrat* 1906-12.

Kemp's Northern *Gazette* 1906-20+.

Evening *Mail* 1910-17 [NCL 1910-17].

Illus *Chronicle* 1910-20+ [NCL].

Sunday *Sun* 1919-20+ [NCL].

See also Durham: Gateshead.

North Shields *see Tynemouth; Durham: South Shields.*

TYNEMOUTH

Nhumbd *Advertiser* 1831-34 [NTL].

(Port of) Tyne *Pilot* (Durham) 1839-42 [NTL; NCL 1839].

Shields Daily *News* 1864-1920+ [NTL].

(Borough of) Tynemouth *Sentinel* 1895-1900.

Walker *see Wallsend.*

WALLSEND

(W) *Herald* (Walker, Willington Quay) 1901-13 [NTL].

WHITLEY BAY

W Seaside *Chronicle* 1910-20+.

WB *Observer* 1919-22.

Willington Quay *see Wallsend.*

For other newspapers covering Nhumbd, see also Durham: South Shields.

NOTTINGHAMSHIRE

Early county newspapers – see Newark, Nottingham; Derbys, Leics, Lincs, Yorks: West Riding.

Ashfield *see Sutton-in-Ashfield.*

Basford *see Nottingham.*

BEESTON

B/West Notts *Gazette & Echo* 1913-20 [Beeston Library 1910-20+ (indexed)].

See also Stapleford.

Bulwell *see Nottingham.*

East Retford *see Retford.*

EASTWOOD [EL = Eastwood Lib]

E & Kimberley *Advertiser* 1895-1920+ [EL (indexed)].

Erewash *see Sutton-in-Ashfield.*

HUCKNALL [HL = Hucknell Library]

Rushcliffe *Advertiser* 1888-1909 [HL].

(H/Rushcliffe) (Morning) *Star* 1889-1913 [HL].

H (Torkard) *Dispatch* (Leen Valley) 1903-20+ [HL (indexed)].

Nottinghamshire *continued*

Kimberley *see Eastwood.*

Leen Valley *see Hucknall.*

MANSFIELD [ML = Mansfield Library]

M *Reporter* (Sutton-in-Ashfield) 1858-1920+ [ML].

M & North Notts *Advertiser* 1873-1920+ [ML 1871-1920+ (indexed 1871-1903, 1916-20+)].

M *Chronicle* (Sutton-in-Ashfield, Shirebrook) 1895-1920+ [ML].

See also Newark, Retford, Sutton-in-Ashfield.

NEWARK [NL = Newark Library]

N (& Mansfield) *Times* 1839-41 [NL].

N *Advertiser* (South Notts) 1859-1920+ [NL 1855-1920+].

N *Herald* 1873-1920+ [NL].

See also Nottingham, Retford; Lincs: Lincoln.

NOTTINGHAM [NCL = Nottingham Central Lib]

N Weekly *Courant* [NCL pre1750-62*].

(Cresswell's) (& Burbages) N (& Newark, Worksop, Retford) *Journal* 1772-87 [NCL 1768-87; Newark Lib 1772-75].

N *Review* 1808-70 [NCL; Ilkeston Lib 1808-17, 1820-26, 1853-70].

N (& Newark) *Mercury* 1827-52 [NCL 1830-52].

Notts *Guardian* 1846-1920+.

Notts *Advertiser* 1854-60 [NCL].

Stevenson's/N Penny/Weekly *Times* 1855-61 [NCL].

N *Telegraph* 1857-63 [NCL].

N (& Midland Counties) Daily *Express* 1860-1918 > N *Journal* 1918-20+ [NCL].

N (Daily) *Guardian* 1861-1920+ [NCL 1869, 1880-1920+].

N *Evening Post* 1878-1920+ [NCL].

(N & Derby) Home *Review* 1882-86 [NCL 1881-86].

N *Evening News* 1885-1920+ [NCL].

N/Notts Weekly *Express* 1886-1920+ [NCL].

N *Argus* 1894-97 > N City *News* 1898-1900.

N & Notts/Bulwell & Basford *Local News* 1906-20+ [NCL 1906-11, 1913-20+].

South Notts *Echo* 1911-20+ [Arnold Lib].

See also Leics: Leicester; Yorks W.R.: Doncaster.

RETFORD [RL = Retford Lib]

(East) R (Newark, Worksop & Gainsboro') *Advertiser* 1854-59 [RL].

R, Worksop, Isle of Axholme & Gainsborough *News* 1867-1920+.

R & Gainsborough (& Worksop) *Times* (Newark, Mansfield) 1871-1920+ [RL (indexed 1871-1913); Lindsey Co Lib 1871-1918].

R & Worksop (& Gainsborough) *Herald* (Lincs, North Notts) 1889-1920+ [RL].

See also Nottingham.

Rushcliffe *see Hucknall.*

Sandiacre *see Stapleford.*

Sherwood *see Sutton-in-Ashfield.*

Shirebrook *see Mansfield.*

STAPLEFORD [SL = Stapleford Lib]

S/Sandiacre *Weekly News* (Beeston) 1919-20+ [SL].

SUTTON IN ASHFIELD

Midland *Gazette* (Sherwood, Ashfield, Erewash, Mansfield) 1857-85 [Mansfield Lib 1846-49, 1857-85].

Notts *Free Press* (Derbys) 1887-1920+ [Sutton in Ashfield Lib 1885-1920+ (indexed)].

See also Mansfield.

WEST BRIDGFORD [WBL = W Bridgford Lib]

WB *Advertiser* 1915-20+ [WBL (indexed)].

WORKSOP

W *Guardian* (North Notts, Derby, South Yorks) 1896-1920+ [Worksop Lib (indexed)].

See also Nottingham, Retford.

For other newspapers covering Notts, see also Leics: Loughborough; Lincs: Gainsborough.

OXFORDSHIRE

Early county newspapers – see Oxford; Berks: Reading; Nhants: Northampton.

[Bod = Bodleian Library, Oxford; OCL = Centre for Oxon Studies, Oxford Central Library.]

Bampton *see Witney.*

BANBURY [BL = Banbury Lib]

B *Guardian* 1843-1920+ [BL, OCL 1838-1920+; Bod 1843-56, 1875-77, 1880-1905, 1916-20+].

B *Advertiser* 1855-1920+ [BL, OCL; Oxon Record Office, Cowley, Oxford 1859-1920+].

B *Herald* 1861-69 [BL, OCL].

B *Beacon* 1863-1905 [BL 1863; OCL 1863, 1868-1905].

B *Leader* 1909-12 [BL, OCL].

See also Oxford.

BICESTER

B *Herald* 1855-1917 [OCL 1855-78, Bod 1872-1917].

B *Advertiser* 1855-66, 1879-1920+ [OCL; Bod 1879-1920+].

(Illus) Oxon (& Buckingham, Brackley, Winslow/Bucks, Northants) *Telegraph* 1858-94 [OCL 1858-59, 1869-1893].

See also Nhants: Brackley.

Burford *see Witney.*

CHIPPING NORTON

Oxon *Weekly News* 1869-1920+ [OCL].

DEDDINGTON

North Oxon Monthly *Times* 1850-54 [OCL 1849-54].

HENLEY-ON-THAMES [HL = Henley Lib]

(Kinch's) H *Advertiser* 1870-1908 [HL, OCL].

H *Free Press* 1885-92 > H & South Oxford *Standard* 1892-1920+ [HL, OCL 1885-86, 1888-1920+].

H *Chronicle* (South Oxon) 1904-13 [Bod, OCL].

Oxfordshire continued

OXFORD

(Jackson's) O *Journal* (Wantage) 1753-1920+ [Bod, OCL; (index and synopsis 1753-90)].

O *Mercury* 1795-96 [OCL, Woodstock Town Hall]

O University (& City) (& County) *Herald* 1806-92 [Bod, OCL].

O (City &) (County) *Chronicle* (Berks, Bucks) 1837-1920+ [OCL; Bod 1838-39, 1844-56, 1859-1920+].

(Hall's) Oxonian *Advertiser* 1853-56 [OCL].

Alden's Illus Family *Miscellany* 1854-66.

O *Times* 1862-1920+ [OCL; Bod 1887-1920+].

O (& Cambridge) Undergraduates' *Review*/O *Review* 1866-1914 [Bod; OCL 1885-1914].

O University *Gazette* 1870-1920+ [Bod, OCL].

O *Messenger* (Banbury, Abingdon, Witney) 1873-76.

O *Guardian* 1884-92 [OCL 1884-87].

O/Oxon *Telegraph* (Berks, Bucks) 1900-03 .

See also Henley-on-Thames; Berks: Abingdon, Reading.

THAME

T *Gazette* 1856-1920+ [OCL].

South Oxon *News* (Wallington) 1887-94 [OCL].

WITNEY [WL = Witney Lib]

W *Telegraph* 1866-69 [OCL, WL].

W *Express* 1869-88 [OCL, WL].

W *Gazette* (Burford, Bampton, West Oxon) 1882-1920+ [OCL, WL].

See also Oxford.

For other Oxon newspapers, see also Berks: Abingdon, Maidenhead, Reading, Wallingford; Bucks: Amersham; Nhants: Brackley.

RUTLAND

Early county newspapers – see Hunts; Leics; Lincs; Nhants..

OAKHAM

Rutland(shire) *Echo*/O *Advertiser* (Uppingham, Melton, Leics) 1877-87 [Leics Record Office, Wigston Magna, Leicester; Rutland County Lib, Oakham].

See also Leics: Melton Mowbray.

Uppingham see Oakham; Leics: Melton Mowbray.

For other newspapers covering Rutland, see also Leics: Market Harborough; Lincs: Stamford.

SHROPSHIRE

Early county newspapers – see Shrewsbury.

[NLW = National Library of Wales; SR = Shropshire Records & Research Centre, Shrewsbury.]

BISHOP'S CASTLE

BC *Advertiser* (Clun) 1900-20+.

BRIDGNORTH

B *Journal* (South Salop) 1854-1920+ [Bridgnorth Lib].

Broseley see Wenlock.

CHURCH STRETTON

CS *Advertiser* 1898-1920+.

Clun see Bishop's Castle.
Craven Arms see Ludlow.
Ellesmere see Wem.
Ironbridge see Wenlock.

LUDLOW

L *Advertiser* (Craven Arms) 1862-1920+.

See also Wenlock; Herefs: Hereford.

Madeley see Wenlock.
Market Drayton see Newport.
Much Wenlock see Wenlock.

NEWPORT

N (& Market Drayton) *Advertiser* 1855-1920+ [Market Drayton Lib 1856-58, 1862-1907, 1909-19].

Oakengates see Wellington.

OSWESTRY [OL = Oswestry Lib]

O *Herald* [NLW 1820-22; OL 1820, 1822].

O (& Border Counties) *Advertiser* 1849-1920+ [NLW 1850-51, 1875-1906*, 1907-20+; OL (indexed); Ruthin (Denbs) Record Office 1907-08].

Shropshire/Salopian & Mont *Post* 1881-93 [NLW 1886].

O Commercial *Circular* 1912-20+.

Shifnal see Wellington.

SHREWSBURY

S *Chronicle* 1772-1898 [SR (indexed)].

Salopian/Eddowes's *Journal* 1794-1811, 1815-91 [NLW 1798-1805, 1836-47, 1839-42, 1844-46; SR 1794-1888 (indexed 1794-1843)].

S *News* 1838-44 [SR].

Salop *Conservative* 1840-61 [SR 1840-49].

Salopian *Telegraph* 1841-44.

Salopian *Advertiser* 1852-55.

S *Register* 1855-59.

Salop & Mont *Times* (Ches) 1863-66 [NLW].

S *Free Press* 1865-81.

Salop *Guardian* 1881-91.

Salop *Evening News* 1885-90.

S *Out-Look* 1911-20+.

S *Commercial* 1915-20+.

See also Wellington.

Shropshire continued

WELLINGTON

W *Advertiser* 1860-55 > Salop *News* 1855-74.

W *Journal* (Shrewsbury) 1854-1920+.

W *Standard* (Shifnal, Oakengates) 1887-91.

WEM

W (& Ellesmere) *Herald* (Ches) 1911-14.

WENLOCK

Ironbridge Weekly *Journal* 1869-75 > (Boro' of) W (& Ludlow) *Express* (Madeley, Broseley) 1875-82 [SR].

Salop *Examiner* 1874-77 [SR].

WHITCHURCH

W *Herald* 1869-1920+.

For other newspapers covering Salop, see also Mont: Welshpool; Worcs: Tenbury Wells; Denbs: Wrexham.

SOMERSET

Early county newspapers – see Bath, Bridgwater, Bristol (under Glos), Taunton; Dorset: Dorchester, Sherborne.

[SRO = Somerset Archive & Record Service, Taunton; SS = Somerset Studies Library, Taunton.]

Axbridge *see Burnham-on-Sea.*

BATH [BCL = Bath Central Library]

(Boddely's/Keenes') B *Journal* pre1750-1916 [BCL pre-1750-66, 1768-70, 1772-73, 1775, 1777-83, 1786-89, 1791-98, 1800-16, 1820-37, 1893, 1897-1916; Bristol Lib pre1750-1758, 1897-1915; Wilts & Swindon Record Office 1746-48; SS pre1750-1837, 1893-1916].

B *Advertiser* 1755-60 [BCL 1755-60*].

(Pope's) B (& Bristol) *Chronicle* 1760-1920+ [BCL 1760-1883, 1885-1895, 1897-1920+; SS 1762-1920+].

Salmon's *Mercury* 1777-81.

B *Herald* 1792-1862 [BCL 1792-1802, 1814-18, 1839-1040, 1849-50].

B & Cheltenham *Gazette* 1812-95 [BCL, SS 1812-93].

B (& Devizes) *Guardian* 1834-39.

B *Express* 1855-75 > B *Herald* 1876-1920+ [BCL 1855-1875, 1880, 1884, 1895, 1906-20+].

B *Argus* (Weekly edn.) 1870-1911.

(B) (Evening/Daily) *Argus* 1875-1900.

B *Observer* 1874-1920+.

(B) (& Wilts) (Evening/Daily) *Chronicle* 1077-1020+.

Bladud 1885-1916 [BCL 1885-93].

See also Glos: Bristol.

Bedminster *see Glos: Bristol.*

Brent *see Burnham-on-Sea.*

BRIDGWATER

B & Soms *Herald* 1831/Alfred London *Weekly Journal* 1831-33 [SS].

B *Times* 1846-61 [SS].

Western Counties' *Herald*/B *Mercury* 1857-1920+ [SS 1857-1920+; SRO 1876-83, 1892, 1894-96, 1898-1900, 1902, 1907-20+].

Somerset: Bridgwater continued

B *Standard* (Burnham) 1861-70 [SS].

B *Gazette* (Devon) 1874-85 [Tiverton Museum 1871-84].

B *Independent* 1885-1920+ [SRO 1901-20+; SS 1907, 1909-10, 1912-20+].

See also Burnham-on-Sea, Taunton.

Brislington *see Glos: Bristol.*

BURNHAM-ON-SEA

B/Highbridge (& Axbridge) *Gazette* 1874-81.

B(S) *Gazette* (Highbridge) 1895-1920+ [SS].

(Bridgwater), Highbridge, B & Dist *Echo* 1894-1905.

B *Herald* (Highbridge) Times 1905-09.

(Highbridge & B) *Local News* 1906-10 > Highbridge *Echo* (Huntspill, Mark, Brent) 1910-20.

H *Express* 1920+.

See also Bridgwater.

CHARD

C & Ilminster *News* 1875-1920+ [SS].

Nowlan's Weekly *Chronicle* 1859-83 [SRO 1863-67].

See also Yeovil.

CHEDDAR

C Valley *Times* 1914-20+.

CLEVEDON

C *Mercury* 1869-1920+.

C *Mail* 1913-20+.

See also Weston-super-Mare.

CREWKERNE

West of England *Express* (Devon, Dorset) 1878-81 > Soms County *Mail* 1881-95.

East Devon *Mail* 1881-96.

Culm Valley *see Wellington*

FROME

Soms & Wilts *Journal* 1855-1920+ [SS 1855-97, 1900-1920+].

East Soms *Telegraph* 1859-86.

F *Times* 1859-86 [SS 1859-86].

Soms *Standard* (Wilts, Dorset) 1886-1920+ [SS 1887-1895, 1898-1920+].

GLASTONBURY

Central Soms *Gazette* 1862-1920+ [SS].

Avalon *Independent* (Street, Mid-Soms) 1890-1920+.

Highbridge *see Burnham-on-Sea.*

Huntspill *see Burnham-on-Sea.*

Ilminster *see Chard.*

Keynsham *see Glos: Bristol.*

LANGPORT

L (& Somerton) *Herald* (Martock, South Petherton) 1855-1920+ [SS 1855-96, 1898-1920+].

Mark *see Brent.*

MARTOCK

Palmer's *Weekly News* 1894-1917.

See also Langport, Yeovil.

Somerset *continued*

Milborne Port *see Dorset: Sherborne.*
Milverton *see Wellington.*

MINEHEAD

M & West Soms *Advertiser* 1887-1920+.

RADSTOCK

Soms *Guardian* 1894-1920+ [SS 1893-1920+].

Saltford *see Glos: Bristol.*

SHEPTON MALLET

SM *Journal* (East Soms, Wells) 1858-1920+ [SS, Wells Lib 1858-1920+].

Somerton *see Langport.*
South Petherton *see Langport.*
Street *see Glastonbury.*

TAUNTON

Western Counties *Advertiser* > Western *Observer* [Tiverton Museum 1795-1920+].

T *Courier* (Wilts, Dorset, Devon, Cornwall, Bristol, Exeter) 1810-1920+ [SS 1810-32, 1834-89, 1891-95, 1898-1911, 1913-20+].

T & Bridgwater *Journal* 1812-16.

Soms County *Gazette* 1836-1920+ [SS 1836-43, 1864-1867, 1873-95, 1898-1920+].

Soms County *Herald* (Bristol, Exeter) 1843-1920+ [SS 1843-95, 1897-1920+].

Western *News* 1855-1920 [SRO 1893-1901].

T *Gazette* 1857-65.

West Soms *Free Press* 1860-1920+ [SS].

Soms *Express* (Bristol) 1887, 1896-1920+ [SRO 1893].

T *Echo* 1887-1920+.

T *Mail* 1894-1920+ [SRO 1894-1901].

See also Devon: Tiverton; Dorset: Dorchester, Sherborne; Glos: Bristol.

WELLINGTON

W *Express* (Culm Valley, West Soms) 1887-1920+.
(Corner's) W *Weekly News* (Wiveliscombe, Milverton) 1869-1920+ [SS 1861-1920+].

WELLS

W *Journal* 1851-1920+ [SS; Wells Lib].
See also Shepton Mallet.

WESTON-SUPER-MARE

WSM *Gazette* (Clevedon, East Soms) 1845-1920+.
(The) *Westonian* 1843-48.
W *Mercury* (Central Soms) 1855-1920+.

WIVELISCOMBE

W *Express* 1898-1920+.
See also Wellington.

YEOVIL

Pulman's *Weekly News* 1857-1920+ [SRO, SS].
Y, Sherborne & Martock *Telegram* 1861-65.
Western *Gazette* (Wilts, Dorset, Berks, Hants, Bournemouth, Blandford) 1863-1920+ [SRO, SS].

Somerset: Yeovil *continued*

Y & Chard *Chronicle* 1885-92 > Western *Advertiser* 1892-1920+ [SRO 1893-1901].
Western *Chronicle* (Dorset) 1886-1920+.
Y *Leader* 1904-20+.
Y *Times* 1847-51.
See also Dorset: Sherborne.

For other newspapers covering Soms, see also Devon: South Molton; Dorset: Bridport.

STAFFORDSHIRE

For the Birmingham conurbation see also under Warwickshire and Worcestershire.

Early county newspapers – see Lichfield, Stafford, Stoke-on-Trent, Wolverhampton; Warw: Birmingham.

[BL = Birmingham Library (Local Studies); DL = Derby Library; HL = Hanley Library; KU = Keele University Library; WA = Wolverhampton Archives & Local Studies; WLH = Walsall Local History Centre; WSL = William Salt Library, Stafford.]

Audley *see Newcastle-under-Lyme.*

BILSTON

B/Midland (Weekly) *Herald* 1871-1906 [WA 1871-79; Bilston Lib, index in progress].
B/Midland *Observer* 1887-93.
South Staffs *Times* 1919-20+.
See also Wolverhampton.

Bromwich *see West Bromwich.*

BROWNHILLS

B & Chasetown *Post* 1888-90 [WLH].
B & Dist Weekly *Reporter* 1904-09 [WLH].

BURTON-UPON-TRENT [BTL = Burton Lib]

BT *Times* (Tamworth) 1855-74 [BTL].
B(T) (Weekly) *News* 1856-90 [BTL; DL 1858, 1870].
B *Chronicle* 1860-1920+.
BT *Express* 1874-79.
B *Standard* (Derbys) 1880-87.
B & Derby *Gazette* 1881-87 [DL 1883].
B *Evening Gazette* 1887-1920+ [BTL 1890-98; DL 1896, 1911].
B (Ashby & Coalville) *Guardian* 1894-1914.
B (Daily) *Mail* 1898-1920+ [BTL].
B *Observer* (South Derbys) 1898-1920+ [DL 1899, 1911-1912].
See also Derbys: Derby.

CANNOCK CHASE

CC *Examiner* 1874-77.
C *Advertiser* 1878-1920+ [WSL 1899-1902, 1909-1920+].
C(C) (& Hednesford) *Mercury* 1883-1905.
CC *Courier* (Pelsall, West Staffs) 1889-1920+.
CC *Herald* 1892-97.
See also Lichfield, Rugeley.

Staffordshire *continued*

Chasetown *see Brownhills.*

CHEADLE
C *Herald* (Tean) 1877-1920+.
C & Tean *Times* 1906-20+.
See also Leek, Stone.

Chesterton *see Newcastle-under-Lyme.*

DARLASTON
D *Weekly Times* (Falling's Heath, King's Hill) 1882-87 [Walsall LH Centre].
See also Wednesbury.

Dudley *see under Worcs.*
Eccleshall *see Stone.*
Falling's Heath *see Darlaston.*
Fenton *see Stone.*

GOSS
G *Record* [Hanley Lib 1901-20+].

Handsworth, Harborne *see Warw: Birmingham.*

HEDNESFORD
H *Advertiser* 1884-99.
See also Cannock, Lichfield, Rugeley.

King's Hill *see Darlaston.*

LEEK
L *Times* 1870-1920+.
L *Post* (Cheadle) 1890-1920+.

LICHFIELD
Staffs *Gazette* 1831-32 [BL ?1815-31].
Staffs *Examiner* 1830-42.
L *Mercury* 1877-1920+ [BL 1815-18; WSL 1823-28; Lichfield Lib 1877-1920+].
L *Herald* (Hednesford, Cannock Chase) 1883-97.
South Staffs *Times* 1911-15 [WLH 1911-13].
See also Warws: Birmingham.

Longton *see Stoke-on-Trent, Stone.*

NEWCASTLE-UNDER-LYME
[NL = Newcastle Lib]
N *Journal* 1855-56 > N & North Staffs *Pioneer* 1856-59 > Staffs (Weekly) *Times* 1859-82 [KU; NL 1855-82].
N *Guardian* (Silverdale, Chesterton, Audley) 1881-1909 [NL].
See also Stoke-on-Trent.

Oldbury *see Smethwick, West Bromwich; Worcs:*
Pelsall *see Cannock.*

RUGELEY
R *Advertiser* 1882-97.
R *Mercury* (Hednesford, Cannock) 1882-1920+.

Sedgeley *see Wolverhampton.*
Silverdale *see Newcastle-under-Lyme.*

SMETHWICK
W eekly *News* (West Bromwich, Oldbury) 1879-1920+.
S *Telephone* (West Bromwich) 1884-1920+.
See also West Bromwich; Worcs: Birmingham.

STAFFORD
Staffs *Advertiser* 1795-1920+ [KU; Holmcroft Lib, Stafford; WSL (indexed 1795-1840); WLH 1830-56].
Staffs *Gazette* 1839-42 [WSL].
S/Staffs *Chronicle* 1877-1920+ [Holmcroft Lib, Stafford 1888, 1891-1920+; WSL 1877-90].
See also Stone.

STOKE-ON-TRENT
Pottery *Mercury* [WSL 1824-28, 1831].
(North) Staffs *Mercury* (Newcastle) 1830-48 [HL, KU].
Potter's *Examiner* 1843-45 [HL 1843-47; KU 1843-47, 1849-50].
Staffs Potteries *Telegraph* 1852-55 [HL].
Staffs *Sentinel* 1854-1920+ [HL; Stoke Lib 1854-83*].
(Staffs &) Potteries *Examiner* 1871-81 [1871-81].
Staffs (Daily) *Sentinel* 1873-1920+ [HL; Newcastle Lib].
Staffs *Knot* 1882-91 > Potteries *Free Press* 1891 [HL].
Staffs (Daily/Morning) *Knot* 1885-88.
Longton *Times* 1894-1905.
Potteries *Advertiser* (North Staffs) 1908-12 [HL 1911-1912].
Staffs Weekly *Sentinel* 1909-20+.

STONE
S (Longton, Fenton) & Eccleshall *Advertiser* (Uttoxeter, Stafford, Cheadle) 1889-1914.
S *Weekly News* 1901-11.

TAMWORTH
T *Advertiser* 1869-72, 1884-1913.
T *Herald* 1870-1920+ [Tamworth Lib 1879-1920+].
T (Miners') *Examiner* 1873-36.
T *Mercury* 1878-1920+.
T *Times* 1892-95, 1905-12.
See also Burton-upon-Trent; Warws: Nuneaton.

Tean *see Cheadle.*

TIPTON
(South Staffs & North Worcs) *Leader* 1908-11.
T *Herald* 1919-20+ [Tipton Lib ?1903-20+].
See also Wednesbury; Worcs. Dudley.

UTTOXETER
U *New Era* 1855-1910
U *Advertiser* (Ashbourne) 1882-1920+.
See also Stone; Derbys: Derby.

WALSALL [WLH = Walsall LH Centre]
W *Guardian* 1856-69.
W *Free Press* (South Staffs) 1856-1903 [WLH 1856-1902].
W *Advertiser* 1862-1915 [WLH].
W *News* 1865-72 [WLH].
W *Observer* (South Staffs) 1868-1920+ [WLH].
W Illuminated/Illus *News* [WLH 1895-1906].

Staffordshire: Walsall *continued*

W Illus *Journal* 1895-1915 [WLH 1904-15].

W *Pioneer* (South Staffs) 1916-20+ [WLH].

WEDNESBURY [WdL = Wednesbury Lib]

W & West Bromwich/South Staffs/Midland *Advertiser* (Tipton, Darlaston) 1869-1920+ [WdL 1879-1920+].

W, West Bromwich & Darlaston/Midland *Examiner* (Tipton, Wolverhampton) 1874-77 [WLH 1874-77].

(Borough of) W *Herald* (South Staffs) 1876-1916 [WdL].

W *Free Press* 1884-87.

W *Leader* 1898-1908 [WdL 1897-1903].

W *Borough News* (Darlaston) 1919-20+.

See also Worcs: Dudley.

Wednesfield *see Wolverhampton.*

WEST BROMWICH
[WBL = West Bromwich Lib]

(Midland) *Free Press* 1875-1920+ [WBL].

WB Weekly *News* [WBL 1875-76, 1889-99]

WB & Oldbury (Smethwick & Dist)/Midland *Chronicle* 1896-1920+ [WBL].

See also Smethwick, Wednesbury; Worcs: Dudley.

WILLENHALL

W *Reporter* 1885-87 [WLH].

See also Wolverhampton.

WOLVERHAMPTON
[WA = Wolverhampton Archives]

W *Chronicle* 1789-1920+ [WA 1789-93, 1811-1920+], partially indexed.

W (& Staffs) *Herald* 1851-69 [WA 1851].

W *Journal* 1853-72 > W Monthly *Messenger* 1872-73.

W *Spirit of the Times* 1859-68 > W *Advertiser* 1869 [WA 1859-61; Wolverhampton Univ 1868-69].

Midland Counties *Express* 1867-1920+ [?WA].

(Midland Counties) (Evening) *Express* (& Star) 1874-1920+ [WA 1882-1920+].

W *Times* (Bilston, Willenhall, Wednesfield, Sedgley) 1875 > W & Midland Counties *Advertiser* 1875-77 > Midland *Examiner* 1877-79 [WLH 1877-78].

Evening *Star* 1880-84 [WA 1880].

W/Midland Counties *Guardian* 1881-84.

(The) *Magpie* 1882-87.

Midland *Evening News* (Birmingham) 1884-1915 [WA 1890, 1890-1905, 1911, 1913].

Midland *Wednesday News* 1884-1908.

Midland *Weekly News* 1884-1915.

W *Comet* [WA 1893-96].

W *Journal* 1902-09 [WA].

Staffs *Herald* 1907-10.

Shaw's (Monthly Home)/W Free *Journal* 1913-18.

See also Wednesbury.

For other newspapers covering Staffs, see also Derbys: Derby; Warws: Birmingham; Worcs: Brierley Hill, Stourbridge.

SUFFOLK

Early county newspapers – see Bury St Edmunds, Ipswich.

[BRO = Suffolk Record Office, Bury St. Edmunds; IRO = Suffolk Record Office, Ipswich; LRO = Suffolk Record Office, Lowestoft.]

ALDEBURGH

A, Leiston & Saxmundham/Suffolk Sea Coast *Times* 1900-12 [IRO].

See also Leiston, Wickham Market.

BECCLES

B *Weekly News* 1857-67 > East Suffk *Gazette* 1867-1920+.

B *Record* 1896-99 > North Suffk *Advertiser* 1899-1902.

See also Lowestoft; Norfolk: Diss.

Brandon *see Norfolk: Diss.*

BURY ST. EDMUNDS

B (& Norwich) *Post* 1782-1920+ [BRO; IRO 1796, 1805-1820, 1838].

B *Gazette* 1821-27 [BRO; IRO 1824].

(B &) Suffk *Herald* (Yarmouth) 1827-49 [BRO 1827-45; IRO 1838].

B *Free Press* (West Suffk) 1855-1920+ [BRO].

B & Suffk *Standard* 1869-87 [BRO].

B & West Suffk *Journal* 1886-90 [BRO].

B & West Suffk *Advertiser* 1886-1907 [BRO].

Eye *see Norfolk: Diss.*

Felixstowe *see Ipswich.*

FRAMLINGHAM

F *Weekly News* 1859-1920+ [IRO].

Gorleston *see Norfolk: Great Yarmouth.*

HALESWORTH

H *Times* (East Suffk, Southwold) 1855-1920+ [LRO].

See also Lowestoft.

HAVERHILL

H *Weekly News* 1889-1910 [Cambridge Central Lib].

South-West Suffk *Echo* 1890-1920+ [BRO 1893-1920+].

IPSWICH

I *Journal* pre-1750-1902 [IRO; BRO 1767-1827; Colchester Lib pre1750-1782; Essex Record Office, Chelmsford pre1750-66].

Suffk *Chronicle* 1819-1920+ [Colchester Lib 1810-59; BRO 1816-19; IRO 1901-02, 1910-20+].

I *Express* (Essex) 1839-74.

I *Advertiser* 1855-63 [IRO].

I (& Colchester) *Times* 1858-74 [IRO 1858-59, 1874].

(East) Suffk *Mercury* 1860-76 > Suffk *Times* 1876-99.

I *Free Press* 1874-86 > Eastern Counties *Gazette* 1886-1889.

East Anglian Daily *Times* 1874-1920+ [IRO].

(Evening) *Star* (of the East) 1885-1920+ [IRO].

I *Observer* (Felixstowe) 1906-09 [IRO].

(I) *Independent* 1908-11.

See also Essex: Colchester.

Suffolk *continued*

LEISTON
L (Aldeburgh & Saxmundham) *Observer* 1913-20+.
See also Aldeburgh.

Long Melford *see Sudbury.*

LOWESTOFT
Eastern *Times* 1869-71 > L *News* 1871-95.
L *Observer* 1870-75.
L *Mercury* 1871-76.
L (Weekly) *Journal* (Yarmouth) 1873-1920+ [LRO].
L (Weekly) *Standard* (East Suffk) 1882-1916.
L *Weekly Press* (Beccles, Halesworth, Southwold) 1886-1918 [LRO].
See also Norfolk: Great Yarmouth, Norwich.

MILDENHALL
M *Post* 1919-20+.

Newmarket *see Cambridgeshire.*
Saxmundham *see Aldeburgh, Leiston.*
Southwold *see Halesworth, Lowestoft.*

STOWMARKET
S *Courier* 1869-70, 1884-1920+.
S *Weekly Post* 1905-17 [IRO].

SUDBURY
(West) (Suffk) & (North) (Essex) *Free Press* 1855-1920+.
Essex & Suffk *News* 1859-1920+.
S *Post* (Long Melford) 1919-20+ [IRO].

Wickham Market *see Woodbridge.*

WOODBRIDGE
W *Reporter* (Aldeburgh, Wickham Market) 1868-1920+ [IRO 1869-1900].

For other newspapers covering Suffolk, see also Essex: Colchester; Norfolk: Great Yarmouth, Norwich.

SURREY

Early county newspapers – see Sussex: Lewes.

[SHC = Surrey History Centre, Woking.]

Addlestone *see Chertsey.*
Ashtead *see Epsom.*
Barnes *see Richmond-upon-Thames.*

CAMBERLEY
C *Gazette* 1902-07.
C *News* (Yorktown) 1905-20+.
See also Woking.

Carshalton *see Wallington.*

CATERHAM
C (& Purley) Free/Weekly *Press* 1892-1920+.
See also Purley.

CHERTSEY
C *Mail* (West Surrey, Addlestone, Egham, Esher) 1869-1872.
Surrey *Herald* (Middx) 1892-1920+ [Chertsey Lib].

COULSDON
C (& Purley) Weekly *Record* 1912-20+.
See also Purley.

CROYDON [CL = Croydon Lib]
C *Chronicle* (East Surrey) 1855-1912 [CL, index 1855-1869].
C *Times* 1861-1920+ CL 1890-1920+, partial index].
C *Observer* 1863-1904 [CL 1860-1901].
C *Journal* 1863-1902.
Surrey *News* 1869-93.
C *Advertiser* (East Surrey) 1869-1920+ [CL, partial index.
C *Guardian* 1877-1916.
C *Express* 1878-1916.
C *Review* 1880-95 [CL ?1879-90].
C *Citizen* 1904-09.
C/Surrey Daily *Argus* 1905-08.

CRYSTAL PALACE
CP *Herald* 1853-56.
CP Dist *Times/Advertiser* 1882-1920+.
See also Lond: Lambeth, Lewisham.

DORKING
D *Journal* 1863-1902.
D (& Leatherhead) *Advertiser* (Epsom) 1887-1920+.
See also Reigate.

EGHAM
E & Staines *News* (Ascot, Sunninghill) 1897-1908 [Chertsey Lib].
See also Chertsey; Mlddx: Staines.

EPSOM [EL = Epsom & Ewell Library]
Surrey *Reporter* 1870-73.
E *Journal* 1871-1902 [EL 1872-1902].
E *Herald* (West & Mid-Surrey) 1881-85 [EL].
E Dist *Times* 1901-17.

Surrey: Epsom *continued*

E *Observer* (Ewell, Ashtead, Leatherhead) 1901-08 [EL].
Mid-Surrey/E & Ewell *Weekly Post* 1904-08 [EL].
E & Ewell *Advertiser* [EL 1910-20+].
E & Ewell *Herald* [EL 1917-20+].
See also Dorking, Leatherhead, Reigate, Sutton.

Esher *see Chertsey.*
Ewell *see Epsom.*

FARNHAM
Surrey & Hants *News* 1864-1920+.
F, Haslemere & Hindhead *Herald* 1897-1920+.
See also Guildford.

Godalming *see Guildford.*

GUILDFORD
(West) Surrey *Times* 1855-1920+.
G *Observer* (Godalming, Farnham, Aldershot) 1860-64.
Surrey *Mail* (Horsham) 1863-75.
G *Journal* (Godalming & Farnborough) 1863-1902.
Surrey *Advertiser* 1864-1920+ [SHC].
Surrey *Standard* 1868-1902.
G (& Godalming)/Surrey Free/Weekly *Press* 1900-1920+.

Haslemere *see Farnham.*
Hindhead *see Farnham.*

HORLEY
H *Advertiser* 1895-1920+.

KINGSTON-UPON-THAMES
[KHC = Kingston Heritage Centre]
Surrey *Comet* 1854-1920+ [KHC].
K & Surbiton *News* 1882-1900.
K (& Richmond) *Express* 1886-94 [KHC 1886-93].
K & Surbiton *Guardian* 1900-07.

LEATHERHEAD
L *Advertiser* (Epsom) 1898-1920+.
See also Dorking, Epsom.

Merton *see London: Wandsworth.*

MITCHAM
M *Advertiser* 1909-20+.
M & Tooting *Mercury* (Streatham, Balham) 1913-20+.
See also Lond: Wandsworth.

Norwood *see London: Lambeth, Lewisham.*

OXTED
O/Village *Searchlight* 1897-1901.
See also Purley.

PURLEY
P, Caterham & Oxted *Gazette* 1903-13.
P & Couldson *Times* 1920+.
See also Caterham, Coulsdon.

REDHILL
Surrey *Leader* 1891-1901.
See also Reigate.

REIGATE
R, Redhill, Dorking & Epsom *Journal* 1863-1902.
(Mid-)Surrey *Mirror* (Reigate, Redhill) 1879-1920+ [SHC 1879-95, 1899-1920+].
Tuesday *Mirror* 1899-1901 > Surrey *Mail* 1891-02.
R & Redhill *Gazette* 1907-13.

RICHMOND-UPON-THAMES
R & Twickenham *Times* 1873-1920+.
Mid-Surrey *Times* (Twickenham) 1876-1904.
(R) (Twickenham & Barnes) *Herald* 1885-1920+.
Thames Valley *Times* 1886-1920+.
See also Kingston-upon-Thames.

Sunninghill *see Egham.*

SURBITON
S *Times* 1895-1920+.
See also Kingston-upon-Thames.

SUTTON [SL = Sutton Library]
S *Journal* 1863-1902.
S *Herald* (Mid-Surrey) 1878-85 [SL 1881-1906, 1908-09].
S (& Epsom) *Advertiser* 1881-1920+ [SL].
S *Observer* [SL 1903-07].
S *Guardian* 1909-10 [SL 1908-09].

THORNTON HEATH
TH *Observer* 1895-1920+.
TH *Echo* 1899-1906 > TH *Press* 1906-10.

Tooting *see Mitcham; London: Wandsworth.*

TWICKENHAM
T *Gazette* 1911-14.
See also Richmond-upon-Thames

WALLINGTON
W & Carshalton/Surrey County *Herald* 1880-1920+ [Sutton Lib 1881-97].
W & Carshalton Weekly *Record* 1907-15.
W & Carshalton *Advertiser* 1908-20+ [Sutton Lib].
W & Carshalton *Times* 1919-20+.

Weybridge *see Woking.*

WIMBLEDON
Surrey *Independent* 1882-1905.
W & Dist *Gazette* 1892-1917.
W (Borough) *News* 1894-1920+.
W *Herald* 1901-20+.
W *News-Letter* 1912-17.

WOKING
W *News* (North-West Surrey) 1894-1920+ [Woking Lib 1898-1920+].
W *Observer* (Weybridge, Yorktown, Camberley) 1896-1920+.
W *Herald* 1901-04.

Yorktown *see Camberley, Woking.*

For other newspapers covering Surrey, see also Berks: Reading; Hants: Aldershot, Basingstoke; Kent: Canterbury; London: Battersea, London (City of), Wandsworth; Middx: Staines; Sussex: Crawley, Lewes.

SUSSEX

Early county newspapers – see Brighton, Hastings, Lewes; Kent: Canterbury.

[BL = Brighton Library; ESRO = East Sussex Record Office, Lewes; WSRO = West Sussex Record Office, Chichester.]

Aldrington *see Hove.*

ARUNDEL
West Sussex *Advertiser* 1853-55 > West Sussex *Gazette* 1855-1920+ [WSRO; Chichester Lib 1860-1920+; Worthing Lib 1854, 1860-87].
See also Littlehampton.

Battle *see Eastbourne.*

BEXHILL-ON-SEA
BS *Chronicle* 1887-1920+.
BS Illus Visitors' *List* 1896-1900.
BS *Observer* 1896-1920+.
BS Kursaal Daily *News* 1903-04 > B Daily *Chronicle* 1904-07.
See also Eastbourne, Hastings.

BOGNOR REGIS
B *Express* (West Sussex) 1871-1902.
B *Observer* 1872-1920+ [Chichester Lib 1890-1920+; WSRO 1880-84, 1886, 1900-01, 1905-20+].
B *Gazette* [Bognor Regis Lib 1894-95].
See also Worthing.

Bramber *see Steyning.*

BRIGHTON
[DL = Brighton Lib]
B *Herald* (Hove) 1806-1920+ [BL 1806-07, 1836-65, 1868-88, 1879-85, 1888-1902; ESRO 1829-31, 1838-1864, 1868-82, 1889-1920+; Hove Lib 1918-20+].
B *Gazette* 1825-1920+ [BL 1821-1920+; ESRO 1848].
B (& Hove) *Guardian* 1827-1901 [ESRO 1835-40, 1842].
B *Patriot* (Lewes) 1835-39
B *Examiner* (Hove, Preston) 1853-95 [BL 1853-96; ESRO 1854-96]
B *Observer*/(B & Hove) Daily *Mail* 1856-1917 [ESRO 1856-57, 1863].
B Fashionable Arrival/Visitors' *List* 1858-78 > B *Standard* 1878-1920+.
B (& Hove) *Times* 1863-1915.
Teacher's B *Record* 1867-1905.
B *Daily News* (South Sussex) 1868-80.
Sussex *Daily News* 1872-1920+ [BL 1881, 1912-20+; WSRO 1881-1920+; ESRO 1907-11, 1913-20+; Hove Lib 1881-1920+].
B & Sussex Daily/Evening *Post* (Hove) 1876-86.
Southern *Weekly News* 1876-1920+.
Cliftonville & Hove *Mercury* 1878-80 [Hove Lib].
(The) *Dolphin* 1878-82.
(The) *Brightonian* 1880-84.
Sussex *Evening Times* 1880-1915.
(Evening) *Argus* 1880-1920+ [BL].

Sussex: Brighton *continued*
B (Hove & Cliftonville/Pictorial) *Advertiser* (Eastbourne) 1880-1920+.
B *Society* 1887-1920+.
Morning *Argus* 1896-1920+.
See also Eastbourne, Hove, Lewes, Shoreham-by-Sea.

CHICHESTER
[ChL = Chichester Lib]
C *Journal*/Southern *Star* (West Sussex) 1860-64 [ChL 1860-62, 1864].
C *Express* (West Sussex) 1863-1902 [ChL].
West Sussex *Journal* 1872-1902.
West Sussex County *Chronicle* (Midhurst, Petersfield) 1877-80.
C *Observer* (West Sussex) 1887-1920+ [WSRO 1888-1889, 1891-92, 1895-1901, 1904-09, 1911-20+].

Cliftonville *see Brighton.*

CRAWLEY
Simmins's Weekly *Advertiser* 1881-82 > Sussex & Surrey *Courier* 1882-1920+ [ESRO 1884-1920+].

CROWBOROUGH
C (& Uckfield) *Weekly* 1903-19.

EASTBOURNE
[EL = Eastbourne Lib]
E *Gazette* 1862-1920+ [EL; ESRO 1874-1920+].
E *Express* (Hailsham, Bexhill, Battle, East Sussex) 1863-1902.
E *Chronicle* 1865-1920+ [EL].
E Fashionable Arrival *List* (Hastings, St. Leonard's, Brighton) 1875-80.
F *Standard* 1875-1901.
(Sussex County) *Herald* 1876-1920+ [ESRO 1913-20+; WL 1918].
E *Courier* 1877-87 > E *Echo* (South Sussex) 1887.
E Illus Visitors' *List* 1877-1910.
E *Scorpion* 1883-92.
E *Review* 1885-90.
E *Observer* 1892-1902.
E & Sussex *Society* 1899-1909.
E (Daily) *Times* 1901-07.
(The) *Visitor* 1914-20.
To-day in E 1917-20+.
See also Brighton, Lewes.

EAST GRINSTEAD
North Sussex *Gazette* 1875-93.
EG *Observer* 1882-1920+ [WSRO 1886-1909, 1911-16, 1918-20+].
Southern *Free Press* 1883-92 > EG *Times* 1892-94.
EG *Express* (Lingfield, Forest Row, Hatfield) 1894-1902

East Preston *see Brighton.*
Forest Row *see East Grinstead.*

HAILSHAM
East Sussex *Journal* 1872-1902.
See also Eastbourne, Lewes.

Sussex *continued*

HASTINGS

Cinque Ports' *Chronicle* (East Sussex) 1838-41.

H & St. Leonards *Chronicle* 1848-1904.

H & St. Leonard's *News* 1848-1905.

(Brett's) St. Leonard's & H *Gazette*/Visitors' *Vade Mecum* 1856-96.

H & St. Leonard's *Times* 1857-58, 1877-99.

Osborne's *Directory* 1859-63 > H & St. Leonard's (Pictorial) *Advertiser* 1863-64, 1859-1918.

H & St. Leonard's *Observer* 1866-1920+.

H & St. Leonards/Bexhill *Independent* (East Sussex, Rye) 1873-1917.

H & St. Leonards *Weekly Mail* 1898-1911.

See also Eastbourne, Rye.

Hatfield *see East Grinstead.*

HAYWARDS HEATH

Mid-Sussex *Times* 1881-1920+ [Burgess Hill Lib 1881-1900, 1912; WSRO 1911-15].

HORSHAM [HsL = Horsham Lib]

H, Petworth, Midhurst & Steyning *Express* 1863-1902.

H *Advertiser* 1871-88 > West Sussex (County) *Times* 1888-1920+ [WSRO, Horsham Mus; HsL 1871-1920+].

H *Times* (West Sussex) 1882-1920+ [WSRO 1884-1920+; HsL 1882-84; ESRO 1908-20+].

See also Surrey: Guildford.

HOVE

Passing Notes/H *Courier* (West Brighton) 1880-82 [Hove Lib].

H *Gazette* (Aldrington, Portslade, Southwick, Shoreham, Brighton) 1896-1915 > Brighton & H Society 1915-20+ [Hove Lib 1896-99].

H *Echo* (Shoreham, Southwick, Portslade) 1897-1903 [Hove Lib 1897, 1901-02].

See also Brighton, Portslade.

LEWES

Sussex (Weekly) *Advertiser* (Brighton, Surrey, West Kent) pre-1750-1904 [BL 1749, 1751-52, 1758-64, 1769-1784, 1786-1831, 1833-38, 1841-42, 1848-51, 1854-65, 1867, 1870-71, 1878-79, 1885-88, 1895-99, 1905-10; Chichester Lib 1749-1822; WSRO 1749-1822, 1827-28; ESRO 1751, 1782-84, 1792-93, 1796, 1799, 1827-32; Hove Lib pre1750-64, 1769-84, 1786-1822; Worthing Lib 1769-1818, 1822-1859].

Sussex (Agricultural) *Express* 1837-1920+ [BL 1837-1884, 1903-20+; Chichester Lib 1837-71; ESRO; Surrey History Centre, Woking 1837-1902].

Sussex *Advertiser* (Surrey, West Kent) 1847-64 > Surrey *Gazette* 1864-1905.

L *Times* (Eastbourne, Hailsham) 1855-63 > East Sussex *News* 1863-1920+ [ESRO 1865-1920+].

Surrey *Standard* 1868-1902.

West Sussex *Journal* 1871-1902.

Sussex *Express* (East Sussex, Rye) 1916-20+.

See also Brighton.

Lingfield *see Sussex.*

LITTLEHAMPTON

(L) *News* 1873-1914 [BL 1906-07, 1911-14; Littlehampton Museum 1869-1914; Littlehampton Lib 1875-91].

L *Gazette* [Littlehampton Museum 1896-1919].

L *Observer* (Arundel, West Sussex) 1909-20+ [WSRO].

See also Worthing.

MIDHURST

M *Times* 1889-1920+.

See also Chichester, Horsham.

Newhaven *see Seaford.*

Petersfield *see Chichester.*

Petworth *see Horsham.*

PORTSLADE

(Hove & P) (Weekly) *Star* 1906-10.

See also Hove.

RYE

R *Chronicle* 1859-61 > South Eastern *Advertiser* (Hastings, St. Leonards) 1861-1917 [ESRO 1915-16].

See also Hastings.

St. Leonard's-on-Sea *see Eastbourne, Hastings, Rye.*

SEAFORD

S & Newhaven *Gazette* 1893-1904.

SHOREHAM-BY-SEA

S & Southwick (Dist) *Gazette* (Brighton) 1899-1907.

See also Hove, Steyning, Worthing.

Southwick *see Hove, Shoreham-by-Sea.*

STEYNING

S *Observer* (Shoreham, Bramber) 1902-05.

See also Horsham.

UCKFIELD

U *Weekly* 1903-15.

See also Crowborough.

WORTHING [WL = Worthing Lib]

W *Express* (Bognor, Littlehampton, Shoreham) 1863-1902 [ESRO].

W *Intelligencer* 1867-1901 > W *Observer* 1901-16 [WL 1890-93, 1898, 1902, 1915].

Sussex Coast/W *Mercury* 1870-1910 [WSRO 1872-1900; WL 1915].

W *Gazette* 1889-1920+ [WL 1883-1920+].

County/Western *Gazette*/W *Advertiser* 1911-14 [WL 1911-13].

W *Herald* 1920+ [WL].

For other newspapers covering Sussex, see also Hants: Emsworth, Petersfield, Portsmouth; Kent: Canterbury, Hawkhurst, Maidstone, Tunbridge Wells.

WARWICKSHIRE

Early county newspapers – see Birmingham, Coventry, Leamington, Warwick.

[BL = Birmingham Library (Local Studies); Bod = Bodleian Library, Oxford; SCL = Sutton Coldfield Lib; Warw RO = Warwickshire Record Office, Warwick.]

ALCESTER
A *Chronicle* 1864-1920+ [Warw RO 1864-1907; Redditch Lib 1888-1920+].
See also Stratford-upon-Avon.

Aston *see Birmingham.*

ATHERSTONE [AL = Atherstone Library]
A (Nuneaton & Warws)/North Warws *Times* 1875-93 [AL 1875-91].
A *Observer* (Leics) 1881-86.
A *Herald* (North Warws) 1884-1920+.
A *News* 1886-1920+ [AL; Warw RO].
A *Express* 1900-20+.
See also Nuneaton.

Balsall Heath *see Birmingham.*

BEDWORTH [BdL = Bedworth Library]
B *Guardian* 1873-1920+ [BdL 1889-91, 1899-1904*; Nuneaton Lib 1889-1920+].
B & Foleshill *News* (Coventry) 1900-20+.
See also Nuneaton.

BIRMINGHAM
[BL = Birmingham Lib, Local Studies]
Aris's B *Gazette* pre1750-1888 [BL, index to obits 1741-1863].
(Swinney's) B (& Lichfield) *Chronicle* 1799-1814, 1819-1827 [BL 1775-1821, 1823-25*].
B Commercial *Herald* 1804-09 [BL].
B *Journal* 1825-69 [BL 1825-68; SCL 1832-37].
B *Advertiser* (South Staffs) 1844-48 [BL].
B/Midland Counties *Herald* 1836-1920+ [BL 1836-7, 1843-1920*].
B *Mercury* 1848-58 [BL].
B Daily *Press* 1855-58 [BL].
Saturday Evening/B Weekly *Post* 1857-1920+ [BL 1869-1920+; SCL 1902-10]
B (Daily) *Post* 1857-1920+ [BL; SCL 1860-1920+].
Midland Counties Saturday *Express* 1861-66.
Town Crier 1861-1903.
B (Daily) *Gazette* 1862-1920+ [BL; SCL 1866-89].
B Morning (& Evening) *News* 1871-76 [BL].
B (Daily) *Mail* 1871-1920+ [SCL 1881-1920+].
Edgbaston & Ladywood *Advertiser* 1874-85.
(B &) Aston *Chronicle* 1875-95 [BL].
Harborne *Herald* 1877-1901 [BL1876-1901].
(The) *Owl* 1879-1911.
(B Pictorial &) *Dart* 1881-1911.
Sunday *Echo* 1882-85 [BL].
Midland *Echo* 1883-85 [Wolverhampton Archives 1883, 1885].
South B/Moseley & Balsall Heath *News* 1883-1920+.

Warwickshire: Birmingham *continued*

Aston *Times* 1884-95, 1899-1901 [BL].
B Suburban *Times* 1884-1901.
Warws *Herald* 1884-1901.
(B) (Illus) Weekly/Sunday *Mercury* 1884-1920+ [Bodleian Lib, Oxford 1885-1914].
Handsworth & Smethwick *Free Press* 1885-88.
B Daily *Times* 1885-90 [BL].
(The) *Telegram* 1886-1907 [BL].
Handsworth *News* (Hockley, Smethwick) 1888-1901.
Handsworth *Chronicle* 1889-1911 [BL].
Daily *Argus* 1891-1902.
Aston/East B (Weekly) *News* 1891-1918 [BL].
Handsworth *Herald* 1891 > (Handsworth &) (North) B *News* 1891-1920+ [BL 1890-1920+].
Harborne/West B (Weekly) *News* 1891-1920+ [BL 1891-1917].
Midland *Sun* 1893-96 [BL].
B *Comet* 1894-97.
Kings Norton & Northfield/South B *Chronicle* 1898-1905 [BL].
B (Sunday) *Echo* 1898-1915 [BL 1898-1913].
Sunday *Argus* 1899-1902.
B Sunday *Mail* 1900-16 [BL 1898-1916].
Midland *Express* 1901-04.
B *Magnet* 1901-05.
(B) Evening *Dospatch* 1902-20+ [BL; SCL].
Erdington *News* 1911-20+ [BL 1907-18].
Sunday *Despatch & Mercuty* 1914-17 [BL 1914-16].
Picture World 1914-16 [BL].
See also Staffs: Wolverhampton.

COLESHILL
Cl *Chronicle* 1874-1920+ [Coleshill Lib 1874-82].

COVENTRY [CL = Coventry Lib]
(Jopson's) Coventry *Mercury* 1754-1836 > C *Standard* 1836-1920+ [CL; Warw RO to 1836].
C *Herald* 1824-1920+ [CL 1808-1920+].
C *Observer* 1827-30 [CL].
C (Warwick & Leamington) (Weekly) Times 1855-1914.
(C) *Free Press* 1858-63.
C *Independent* 1873-88 > C *Mercury* 1888-1909.
(Athletic/Midland Counties/C) *Reporter* 1885-1911.
Midland Daily *Telegraph* 1891-1920+ [CL].
C & Warws *Graphic* 1912-21.
See also Bedworth.

Edgbaston *see Birmingham.*
Erdington *see Birmingham, Sutton Coldfield.*
Foleshill *see Bedworth.*
Handsworth *see Birmingham.*
Harborne *see Birmingham.*
Hockley *see Birmingham.*

KENILWORTH
K *Advertiser* 1869-1920+.
See also Leamington Spa.

Warwickshire *continued*

Kineton *see Rugby.*
King's Norton *see Birmingham.*

KNOWLE
K *Journal* (Solihull) 1893-1901 [BL; Solihull Lib].

Ladywood *see Birmingham.*

LEAMINGTON SPA [LSL = Leamington Spa Lib]
(Royal) LS *Courier* 1828-1920+ [LSL; Bod 1828-56].
L *Press* 1834-35 > (Royal) LS *Chronicle* (South Warws)
1835-59 [LSL].
L *Advertiser* 1849-1904.
(Royal) L(S) *Chronicle* (Warwick, Rugby) 1865-1920+.
L *News* (Warwick) 1882-1900 [Warws RO].
L(S) (Warwick) (Kenilworth) (& Dist) Daily *Circular* 1896-
1919 > L, Warwick, Kenilworth & Dist *Morning News*
1919-20+ [BL 1899-1919; LSL 1919-20+].
See also Coventry, Warwick; Nhants: Northampton.

Moseley *see Birmingham.*
Northfield *see Birmingham.*

NUNEATON [NL = Nuneaton Lib]
N *Advertiser* 1868-20+ [NL].
N *Chronicle* (Tamworth, Atherstone, Hinckley, Bedworth)
1868-1920+ [NL; Bedworth Lib 1868-96, 1898-1919].
N *Times* 1875-78.
(N) *Observer* 1877-1920+ [NL; BL 1877-96, 1898-1916].
(People's/Midland Counties) *Tribune* 1895-1920+.
(N/Warws) *Star* 1911-17 [NL 1911].
Midland *Daily Tribune* 1915-20+.
See also Atherstone.

RUGBY [RL = Rugby Lib]
R (Monthly) *Advertiser* (Lutterworth) 1846-1920+ [RL].
R *Gazette* 1858-76 > Midland *Times* 1876-1906 [RL].
R *Review* 1894-96, 1905-06 [RL 1905-06].
R *News* 1898-1908.
R *Recorder* 1906-10.
R *Observer* 1911-20+ [RL].
R & Kineton *Advertiser* 1913-20+.
See also Leamington Spa.

SHIPSTON-ON-STOUR
S(S) *News* 1879-95.
See also Stratford-upon-Avon.

Solihull *see Knowle.*

STRATFORD-UPON-AVON
[SBT = Shakespeare Birthplace Trust Archives]
S, Shipston & Alcester *Journal* [SBT 1750-53*].
SA *Chronicle* 1866-85 [SBT 1861-85].
SA *Herald* 1866-1920+ [SBT 1860-1912 (indexed 1860-
1912); BL 1891-1920+; Bod 1909, 1912-20+].

SUTTON COLDFIELD [SL = Sutton Coldfield Lib]
SC & Erdington *News* 1870-71, 1877-84 [SL, BL].
SC & *Erdington* Times (North Warws) 1883-1901.
SC & Erdington *Mercury* 1887-95, 1898-1904 [BL]
SC *News* 1900-20+ [SL, BL].

WARWICK
W & Warws (General) *Advertiser* (Leamington) 1806-
1820, 1824-1920+ [Warws RO; BL; Solihull Lib 1806-
1920+; index to coroners' inquests 1806-32].
W & Leamington (& Warws) *Times* 1869-1918.
See also Coventry, Leamington Spa.

WESTMORLAND

Early county newspapers – see Kendal.

[KRO = Cumbria Record Office, Kendal.]

AMBLESIDE
A/Lakes *Herald* 1880-1916 [Kendal Lib].
See also Windermere.

Bowness, Coniston *see Windermere*

KENDAL [KL = Kendal Lib]
Westmd *Advertiser* 1811-34 > K/Westmd Mercury 1834-
1917 [KL 1811-34*, 1834-69, 1877, 1881-1917; KRO
1811-34].
Westmd *Gazette* 1818-1920+ [KL. KRO].
Dawson's Monthly *Advertiser* [KRO 1846-49].
K *Herald* [KL, KRO 1864-66].
K *Times* 1864-80 [KL 1867-79; KRO 1864-79].
K & County *News* 1887-99 [KL 1888-99; KRO 1888-90,
1894-99].

WINDERMERE
Lakes *Chronicle* (Ambleside, Bowness, Coniston) 1875-
1910.

WILTSHIRE

*Early county newspapers – see Devizes, Marlborough,
Salisbury.*

[TL = County Local Studies Library, Trowbridge; WRO =
Wilts & Swindon Record Office, Trowbridge.]

Bradford-on-Avon *see Trowbridge.*
Calne *see Marlborough.*

CHIPPENHAM
C *Chronicle* (North Wilts, West Glos) 1876-82.
North Wilts *Guardian* 1897-1917.
See also Glos: Bristol.

Cricklade *see Swindon.*

DEVIZES
(D &) Wilts *Gazette* 1821-1920+ [TL 1819-1920+; WRO
1819-21, 1895-1907; Swindon Ref Lib 1819-55].
Wilts *Independent* 1836-76 [TL 1836-71, 1873-76; WRO
1836-37].
D (& Wilts) *Advertiser* 1858-1920+ [TL].
Wilts *Times* 1876-80 [WRO].
Wilts *Telegraph* 1878-1920+ [TL 1877-1920+].
See also Soms: Bath.

Wiltshire *continued*

Knoyle *see Dorset: Shaftesbury.*
Malmesbury *see Glos: Bristol, Tetbury.*

MARLBOROUGH [ML = Marlborough Lib

M *Journal* 1771-74 [ML; TL; Bodleian Lib, Oxford].
M *Times* 1859-1910 > Wilts & Berks (& Hants) *County Paper* 1910-20+ [ML, TL 1859-1920+; WRO 1859-69].
M & Hungerford *Express* 1860-63.
M *Journal* (Hungerford, Calne, Pewsey) 1873-77.
Wilts *Opinion* 1903-20+.
See also Berks: Newbury.

Melksham *see Trowbridge.*
Pewsey *see Marlborough.*

SALISBURY
[WAS = Wilts Arch & Nat Hist Soc, Devizes]
S (& Winchester) *Journal* pre1750-1920+ [TL, Salisbury Lib 1746-49, 1751-1920+; WAS 1746-49, 1787-1836; WRO 1758-59, 1770-71, 1775-1920+; Bodleian Lib, Oxford 1762-1811*].
Simpson's S *Gazette* [TL, WAS 1816-19; WRO 1817-1818].
S & Wilts *Herald* 1833-52 [TL; WAS 1842-44].
Wilts County *Telegram* 1863-69.
S *Times* 1868-1920+ [TL 1868-69, 1874-95, 1895-1920+].
South Wilts *Express* 1873-87.
Wilts County *Mirror* 1852-1911.
See also Hants: Southampton.

SWINDON [SRL = Swindon Ref Lib]
S *Advertiser* 1856-1920+ [SRL, TL 1854-1920+].
North Wilts *Herald* 1861-1920+ [SRL, TL; WRO 1861-1907, 1909-20+].
New S *Express* (Cricklade) 1876-80.
Evening North Wilts *Herald* 1882-1920+.
Evening S *Advertiser* 1899-1920+ [SRL 1900-10].
Borough *Press* 1906-20+.
See also Glos: Bristol.

TROWBRIDGE
T (& North Wilts) *Advertiser* 1855-80 [WRO 1855-64, 1866-80].
T *Chronicle* (Bradford-on-Avon, Melksham, Westbury) 1861-95 [TL 1861-1906; WRO 1861-1905].
Wilts *Times* 1880-1920+ [TL; WRO 1881-1902]
Wilts *Chronicle* 1895-1906.
Wilts *News* 1913-20+ [TL 1909-20+; WRO 1911, 1918-1920+].

WARMINSTER
W *Miscellany* 1855-63 [TL, WRO].
W (& West Wilts) *Herald* 1857-93 [TL].
W & Westbury *Journal* 1881-1920+ [TL].

Westbury *see Trowbridge, Warminster.*

For other newspapers covering Wilts, see also Berks: Maidenhead; Glos: Bristol; Hants: Andover, Basingstoke; Soms: Bath, Frome, Taunton, Yeovil.

WORCESTERSHIRE

Early county newspapers – see Kidderminster, Worcester.

[BL = Birmingham Library (Local Studies); WHC = Worcestershire Library and History Centre, Worcester; WRO = Worcestershire Record Office, Worcester.]

Balsall Heath *see Warw: Birmingham.*
Bewdley *see Kidderminster.*

BRIERLEY HILL
(BH/County) *Advertiser* (Staffs) 1856-1920+ [Kidderminster Lib 1856-67; Dudley Lib 1856-1907; Smethwick Lib 1856-74].
County *Express* (Stourbridge, Kidderminster, Dudley) 1867-85.
County *Herald* (Staffs) 1919-20+.
See also Dudley.

BROMSGROVE
(Scroxton's) B *Gleaner* 1854-61.
B & (District/Droitwich (& Redditch) (Weekly) *Messenger* 1860-1920+ [WHC, WRO 1891-1920+].
Weekly *Independent* (Droitwich, Redditch) 1877-93.
See also Kidderminster.

Cradley Heath *see Stourbridge.*

DROITWICH
D *Guardian* 1883-1920+ [BL].
See also Bromsgrove.

DUDLEY [DL = Dudley Lib]
D *Herald* (Wednesbury) 1866-1920+ [DL].
D *Guardian* (Tipton, Oldbury, West Bromwich) 1869-75 [DL].
D & Dist *News* 1880-85 [DL].
D *Mercury* (Stourbridge, Brierley Hill) 1887-90 [DL].
D *Chronicle* 1910-20+ [DL].
See also Brierley Hill.

EVESHAM
E *Journal* 1860-1920+ [Evesham Lib, WHC, WRO].
Vale of E *News* (Pershore) 1869-73.
E *Standard* 1808-1920+.

Halesowen *see Stourbridge.*
Hockley *see Warw: Birmingham, Handsworth.*

KIDDERMINSTER [KL = Kidderminster Lib]
K/Ten Towns' *Messenger* 1836-49 [KL].
K *Times* (Bewdley, Stourport) 1867-1920+ [KL].
(K) *Shuttle* 1870-1920+ [WHC, WRO, KL].
K *News* (Bromsgrove, Bewdley, Stourport) 1875-85,
(K) *Sun* (Bewdley, Stourport) 1877-1900 [KL 1885-99].
K *News* 1900-10.
See also Brierley Hill.

King's Norton *see Warw: Birmingham.*

MALVERN
(Illus) M *Advertiser* (Ledbury, Upton) 1855-1907.
M *News* 1860-1920+.
M *Looker-on* 1886-90.
M *Gazette* 1898-1920+.

Worcestershire *continued*

Moseley, Northfield *see Warw: Birmingham.*
Oldbury *see Dudley; Staffs: Smethwick, West Bromwich.*
Pershore *see Evesham.*

REDDITCH
R *Indicator* 1859-1920+.
(The) *Arrow* 1889-92 > R *News* (East Worcs) 1892-94.
See also Bromsgrove.

Shipston-on-Stour *see under Warws.*
Smethwick *see Staffs: West Bromwich.*

STOURBRIDGE
S *Mercury* 1862-69 [Dudley Lib].
(Cradley Heath &) (S) *Observer* (Halesowen) 1864-88.
(S, Brierley Hill &) County *Express* (Staffs) 1885-1920+.
See also Brierley Hill, Dudley.

Stourport *see Kidderminster.*

TENBURY WELLS
T(W) *Advertiser* 1871-1920+.
TW *Mail* (West Worcs, North Herefs, South Salop) 1911-1920+.

UPTON-ON-SEVERN
US *News* 1902-20+.
See also Malvern.

WARLEY
Weekly *News* for West Bromwich, Oldbury, Smethwick 1879-1920+ [Smethwick Lib 1880-1920+, index 1880-1906; West Bromwich Lib 1875-1914].
Smethwick *Telephone* (West Bromwich) 1884-1920+ [Smethwick Lib].

WORCESTER
(Berrow's) W *Journal* pre1750-1920+ [WHC; WRO].
W *Herald* 1794-1920+ [WHC; WRO 1803-92*; BL 1799-1800, 1829-36].
Worcs *Guardian* 1834-46 [WHC, WRO 1834-35, 1844-1845].
W/Worcs *Chronicle* 1838-1920+ [WHC, WRO 1839-1913].
W *News* 1861-69.
Worcs *Advertiser* 1865-1920+ [WHC, WRO 1876-1913].
(W) Evening *Post* 1877-83 > Worcs *Echo* 1883-1920+.
W Daily *Times* 1880-1920+ [WHC, WRO 1880-1900].
Worcs *Standard* 1897-1920+.

For other newspapers covering Worcs, see also Herefs: Hereford; Staffs: Tipton, West Bromwich; Warw: Birmingham, Handsworth.

YORKSHIRE EAST RIDING

Early county newspapers – see Hull.

[HCL = Hull Central Library.]

BEVERLEY
B/E.R. (Weekly) *Recorder* 1855-1920+.
B *Guardian* 1856-1920+.
B *Echo* 1885-1903.
B *Independent* 1888-1911.
(B &) E.R. *Telegraph* 1895-1903.

BRIDLINGTON
B & Quay *News* 1858-68.
B-Quay *Observer* 1859-99.
(B) *Free Press* 1859-1920+.
B & Quay *Gazette* 1874-1914.
B (& Quay) *Chronicle* 1897-1920+.

DRIFFIELD
D *Observer* 1869-1914.
D *Times* 1869-1920+.
D *Express* 1872-73 > East (& North) Riding *Chronicle* 1874-1917.

FILEY
F *Chronicle* 1855-58 > F *Post* 1869-1918.

Goole *see Yorkshire; West Riding.*
Holderness *see Hornsea, Hull.*

HORNSEA
H *Gazette* (Hull, Holderness) 1869-1901.

HOWDEN
Howdenshire *Gazette* 1873-1920+.
See also Goole.

Howdenshire *see Howden, Pocklington; Yorks W.R.: Selby.*

HULL
H *Courant* [HCL pre1750-59*].
H *Packet* 1793-1827, 1833-86 [HCL 1787-88, 1794-96, 1800-23, 1826-71, 1873-86].
H *Advertiser* 1794-1867 [HCL; obits index 1800-50].
H/Lincs *Chronicle* 1807-10.
Rockingham & H Weekly *Advertiser* 1808-28 > H, Rockingam & Yorks & Lincs *Gazette* 1828-44 [?HCL 1808-40.
H *Portfolio* [HCL 1831-33].
H, E.R. & North Lincs *Observer* 1834-41 [HCL 1834-40].
H Saturday *Journal* 1836-41.
H & E.R. *Times* 1838-42 [HCL 1838-42*].
(H &) Eastern Counties *Herald* 1838-84 [HCL].
(H) (Daily) *News* (Grimsby) 1852-1920+ [HCL].
H *Free Press* 1853-60.
Yorks & Lincs *Advertiser* 1853-69.
H (E.R. &) (North) (Lincs) *Times* 1857-1920+ [HCL].
Eastern *Evening News* 1864-67.
Eastern *Weekly News* 1864-66.
Eastern *Morning News* 1864-70.
H Morning *Telegraph* 1869-80.

Evening News 1870-76 > H *Express* 1870-91.

(H & E.R.) *Critic* 1883-92 [HCL 1883-89].

H (Weekly) *Express* 1883-1902 > Daily *News* (Grimsby) 1902-12.

(H) Daily *Mail* 1885-1920+ [HCL 1885-86, 1894-1920+].

Lincs *Express* 1886-91.

H *Entr'acte* 1897 > East Yorks *Comet* 1897-1900 [HCL 1886].

H *Star* [HCL 1895-98].

New H *Critic* 1896-99 > H (Illus) *Punch* 1899.

H & East Yorks *Times* 1897-1920+ [HCL].

(East) H *Free Press* (Holderness) 1905-13.

H *Topics* (East Yorks) [HCL 1907-14].

See also Hornsea, Withernsea.

Kingston-upon-Hull *see Hull.*
Market Weighton *see Pocklington.*
Marshland *see Yorks W.R.: Goole.*

POCKLINGTON

Howdenshire *Chronicle* (Market Weighton) 1889-1920+.

Rockingham *see Hull.*
Upper Derwent *see Yorks N.R.: Malton.*

WITHERNSEA

W *Chronicle* (Hull) 1873-91.

For other newspapers covering Yorks E.R., see also Lincs: Gainsborough.

YORKSHIRE NORTH RIDING
(including York)

Early county newspapers – see Scarborough, York.

BEDALE

B (& Northallerton) (& Ripon) *Times* 1858-1914.
See also Ripon.

Brompton *see Northallerton.*
Brotton *see Guisborough.*
Cleveland *see Middlesbrough, Redcar, Richmond.*

EASINGWOLD

E *Chronicle* (Thirsk) 1856-61.
Easingwold Advertiser & Weekly News 1892-1920+.

Eston *see Middlesbrough.*
Grangetown *see Middlesbrough.*

GUISBOROUGH

G *Exchange* (Skelton, Lofthouse, Brotton) 1872-78.
See also Saltburn.

HAWES

Wensleydale *Advertiser* 1844-48.

LOFTHOUSE (LOFTUS)

L *Advertiser* 1879-1916.
See also Guisborough.

MALTON

M (& Norton) *Gazette*/North-Eastern *Advertiser* 1855-1905.

M *Messenger* (Upper Derwent) 1855-1920+.

MIDDLEHAM

Mentor's M *Opinion* 1890-1920+.

MIDDLESBROUGH [ML = Middlesbrough Lib]

M (Weekly) *News* (Cleveland) 1859-84 [ML].

M/Daily *Exchange* (North Ormesby) 1869-87 [ML].

(North-Eastern) Daily/Evening/Saturday *Gazette* (Stockton, Bishop Auckland) 1869-1920+ [ML; Stockton Lib 1870-1920+].

M Temperance *Visitor* 1871-83 [ML].

Cleveland *News* 1873-87 [ML].

South Bank *Advertiser* 1876-84.

Weekly *Exchange* 1876-87.

South Bank *News* (Grangetown, Eston, Normanby) 1884-87 [ML].

Northern *Review* 1886-94 [ML].

Tees-side Weekly *Herald* 1904-18 [ML].

M *Standard* 1908-20+ [ML].

See also CO. Durham: Stockton-on-Tees, Sunderland.

Nidderdale *see Pateley Bridge; Yorks W.R.: Harrogate.*
Normanby *see Middlesbrough.*

NORTHALLERTON

N.R & N *News* (Osmotherley, Brompton) 1904-20+.
See also Bedale, Ripon.

North Ormesby *see Middlesbrough.*
Norton *see Malton.*
Osmotherley *see Northallerton.*

PATELEY BRIDGE

PB & Nidderdale *Herald* 1863-1920+.
See also Yorks W.R.: Harrogate.

Rawcliffe *see Yorks E.R.: Goole.*

REDCAR

R & Saltburn-by-the-Sea *Gazette* 1869-1900.

R & Saltburn *News* 1871-1916.

Cleveland *Standard* 1908-20+.

South Bank *Express* 1909-20+,

RICHMOND

R *Weekly News* (Ripon, Swaledale, Wensleydale) 1855-1856 > R & Ripon *Chronicle* 1856-94.

R *Telegraph* (Swaledale, Wensleydale, Cleveland) 1873-76.
See also Co. Durham: Darlington; Yorks WR: Ripon.

Ripon *see Yorks: West Riding*

SALTBURN

S (& Guisborough) *Times* 1887-1920+.
See also Redcar.

Yorkshire: North Riding *continued*

SCARBOROUGH
S *Herald* 1836-46.
S *Gazette* 1845-1920+.
(James Greasley's) S *Times* 1855-69.
(Illus) S *Mercury* 1855-1920+.
S *Express* 1865-83.
S (Daily) *Post* 1876-1920+.
S *Evening News* 1886-1920+.
S *Weekly Post* 1912-20+.
S *Pictorial* 1913-16.

Skelton see *Guisborough.*
Swaledale see *Richmond.*

THIRSK
T *Advertiser* 1897 > T & District *News* 1898-1920+.
See also Easingwold.

Thornaby see *Durham: Stockton-on-Tees.*
Wensleydale see *Hawes, Richmond; Yorks W.R: Skipton.*

WHITBY
W *Gazette* 1854-1920+ [Whitby Lib (indexed)].
W *Times* (North Yorks) 1869-1912.

YORK
[YL = York Lib; YML = York Minster Lib]
Y *Courant* pre1750-1811, 1828-48 [YL pre1750-56, 1760-74, 1778-1834 (indexed); YML 1750-1821].
(Etherington's) Y *Chronicle* 1772-1840 [YL 1772-1835* (indexed 1773-77, 1817-18)].
Y/Yorks *Herald* 1791-1920+ [YL 1780-1889 (indexed 1790-1801); YML 1790-1819].
Yorks *Gazette* 1819-1920+ [Leeds Central Lib 1820-1870; YL (indexed); YML 1819-1919].
(The) *Yorkshireman* 1834-58 [YML 1834-35].
Yorks *Advertiser* 1859-69.
Y *Star* [YL 1861-74].
Yorks *Telegraph* 1869-76 [YL 1869-73].
Yorks *Chronicle* (South Durham) 1869-1914.
(Yorks) *Evening Press* 1884-1920+ [YL 1882-1920+].
Waddington's *Journal* 1888-95.
Yorks *Daily Chronicle* 1888-93.
Y/Weekly *Sentinel* 1894-98.
Yorks *Observer* 1899-1903 < Yorks *News* 1904-20+.
Yorks *Weekly Herald* 1902-16.
Y *Star* 1910-20+.

For other newspapers covering Yorks N.R. & York, see also Co. Durham: Darlington; Yorks E.R.: Driffield.

YORKSHIRE WEST RIDING

Early county newspapers – see Bradford, Doncaster, Halifax, Harrogate, Huddersfield, Leeds, Sheffield and Wakefield..

[HCL = Halifax Central Library; HdL = Huddersfield Library; LCL = Leeds Central Library.]

Addingham see *Ilkley.*
Airedale see *Otley, Shipley.*
Altofts see *Normanton.*

ARMLEY
A & Wortley *News* 1889-1920+ [LCL 1900-20+].

Barnoldswick see *Craven; Lancs: Colne.*

BARNSLEY
[BA = Barnsley Archives & Local Studies]
B *Times* 1855-1882 > B *Independent* 1883-1920+ [BA].
B *Record* 1858-66 [BA].
B *Chronicle* 1858-1920+ [BA].
B *Herald* 1860-66 [BA].
B *Echo* 1869-74 [BA].
Midland & Northern Coal & Iron Trades *Gazette* 1875-86 [BA 1875-83].
B *Telephone* 1904-20 [BA].
See also Sheffield.

BATLEY
B *Reporter* 1869-1920+ [Batley Lib; HdL].
B *News* 1883-1920+ [Batley Lib; HdL].
B & Heavy Woollen District *Free Press* 1903-20+.

BINGLEY
B (& Dist) *Chronicle* 1889-1909.
See also Keighley.

BIRSTALL
B *Herald* (Gomersal) 1919-20+.

BOROUGHBRIDGE
B *Observer* 1906-18.
See also Knaresborough.

BOSTON SPA
BS *Journal* 1873-79 > BS *News* 1879-1920+.

Bowling see *Bradford.*

BRADFORD [BCL = Bradford Central Lib]
B & Wakefield *Chronicle* [BCL 1825-26].
B & Huddersfield *Courier* [BCL 1825-28].
B/Yorks (Daily) *Observer* 1834-1920+ [BCL (indexed 1834-1907); Keighley Lib 1834-1915].
B *Advertiser* 1855-79.
B *Review* 1858-70 [BCL 1859-69].
B *Times* 1865-71, 1880-83.
B Daily *Telegraph* 1868-1920+ [BCL].
B/Illus Weekly *Telegraph* 1869-1920 [BCL 1869-1920*].
(B/Yorks) *Observer Budget* 1869-1920+ [BCL 1872-1911; Keighley Lib 1912-20+].
B *Weekly Mail* 1871-74.
B *Evening Mail* 1871-75.

Yorkshire: West Riding: Bradford continued

(B) (Daily) *Chronicle* (North W.R.) 1872-83 [BCL].
(The) *Yorkshireman* 1875-1920+.
B *Citizen* 1884-93.
B *Mercury* 1890-1900.
B Daily *Argus* 1892-1920+ [BCL].
(B) *Citizen Weekly* 1893-1906.
Laisterdyke & Bowling *News* 1895-1917.
Kemp's Yorks *Gazette* 1906-20+.
B *Pioneer* 1913-20+ [BCL].
  See also Halifax.

BRIGHOUSE [HCL = Halifax Central Lib]

B & Rastrick *Chronicle* 1859-64 [HCL].
B *News* 1871-1911 [HCL 1870-1908, 1910-11].
B (& Rastrick) *Gazette* 1874-99 [HCL 1874-96, 1898-99].
B *Echo* 1887-1920+ [HCL].
B *Free Press* 1898-1920+ [HCL].
B *Observer* (Elland) 1912-15 [HCL 1912, 1914-15].

Calder Vale *see Hebden Bridge.*
Calverley *see Leeds.*

CASTLEFORD

C *Chronicle* (Knottingley) 1858-62.
C *Star* 1869-72.
C *Gazette* 1872-1902.
C *Telegraph* (Whitwood, Kippax, Methley, Featherstone) 1892-98.
(The) *Stalwart* 1906-10.
  See also Pontefract.

Cawood *see Tadcaster.*
Claro *see Harrogate, Knaresborough.*

CLECKHEATON

C *Guardian* (Liversedge, Gomersal, Scholes, Spen Valley) 1873-1915.
C *Advertiser*/Spen Valley *Times* (Spenborough) 1874-1920+.
C & Spenborough *Guardian* 1911-20+.

Colne Valley *see Slaithwaite.*

CRAVEN [BwL = Barnoldswick Lib]

C/West Yorks (Weekly) *Pioneer* (East Lancs) 1865-1920+ [BwL 1853-57; Keighley Lib 1885-1920+].
C *Herald* 1875-1920+ [BwL 1877-1920+ (indexed); Keighley Lib 1891-1920+*].

Cross Gates *see Leeds.*

DEWSBURY

D *Chronicle* 1869-95.
D *Reporter* 1869-1920+ [Batley Lib; Hdl].
D *District News* 1891-1920+ [Batley Lib; HdL].
  See also Wakefield.

DONCASTER [DL = Doncaster Lib]

D (Nottingham & Lincoln) *Gazette* 1807-1920+ [DL 1794-1920+; Sheffield Lib 1802-06].
D *Chronicle* 1836-1920+ [DL].

Yorkshire: West Riding: Doncaster continued

D *Reporter* 1867-90.
D *Free Press* 1868-90.
D & Thorne *Advertiser* 1894-1920+.
D Borough *Advertiser* 1906-09.

Eastwood *see Lancs: Todmorden.*
Ecclesfield *see Penistone.*
Elland *see Brighouse.*
Farsley *see Leeds, Pudsey.*
Featherstone *see Castleford.*
Goldcross *see Pontefract.*
Gomersal *see Birstall, Cleckheaton.*

GOOLE

G (& Marshland) (Weekly) *Times* 1869-1920+.
G, Marshland & Howden *Gazette* (Snaith, Rawcliffe) 1870-73.
G *Telegraph* 1875-79.
G (Saturday) *Journal* 1889-1920+.
G Weekly *Herald* 1891-1901.
  See also Selby.

Guisley *see Ilkley, Otley.*

HALIFAX [HCL = Halifax Central Lib]

H *Journal* [HCL 1801-11].
H (& Huddersfield) *Express* (Bradford, Wakefield) 1831-1841 [HCL; Huddersfield Lib].
H *Guardian* (Huddersfield, Bradford) 1832-1920+ [HCL, Huddersfield Lib].
H *Courier* 1853-1920+ [HCL].
H *Times* 1872-95 [HCL 1872-73, 1889-95].
H *Observer* 1884-87 [HCL].
H *Mercury* 1890-95 [HCL].
H *Local Opinion* 1892-93 > H *Comet* 1893-1904 [HCL 1893-1904].
H *Evening Courier* 1892-1920+ [HCL].
H *Daily Guardian* 1906-20+ [HCL].
  See also Wakefield.

HARROGATE

H *Advertiser* 1836-1920+ [Harrogate Lib 1837-56].
H *Weekly Gazette* 1837-41.
H *Herald* 1847-1920+ [Harrogate Lib 1882-86].
H (& Claro) *Times* (Knaresborough) 1903-20.
H *Gazette* 1873-79 > H *News* (Ripley, Pateley Bridge, Nidderdale) 1879-90.
H *Visitor* (Knaresborough, Nidderdale) 1894-1900.
H *Star* 1908-17.
  See also Knaresborough.

HEBDEN BRIDGE

HB *Times* (Calder Vale) 1883-1920+ [HCL 1882-84, 1886-87, 1889-1920+].
HB & Dist *News* 1908-20+ [HCL 1908-09, 1912-13, 1915-18, 1920+].
  See also Lancs: Todmorden.

Yorkshire: West Riding *continued*

HECKMONDWIKE
H *Reporter* 1869-99.
H *Express* 1870-74.
H *Herald* (Liversedge) 1885-1920+.

Hemsworth *see Mexborough, South Elmsall.*
Holbeck *see Leeds.*

HOLMFIRTH
H *Express* 1886-1920+.
See also Huddersfield.

HORBURY
H *Express* 1870-76 > H *Free Press* 1871-76.

Hoyland *see Penistone.*

HUDDERSFIELD [HdL = Huddersfield Lib]
Voice of the W.R. 1833-34 [HdL, Bradford Central Lib, Halifax Central Lib].
H *Chronicle* (West Yorks) 1850-1916 [HdL].
H (& Holmfirth) *Examiner* 1851-1920+.
H *Observer* 1867-71.
H *Times* 1869-79.
H *Weekly News* (South West Yorks) 1871-1904.
H *Daily Chronicle* 1871-1915.
H *Daily Examiner* 1871-1920+.
Yorks *Factory Times* 1889-1919 [Leeds Central Lib 1910-20+; Wakefield Lib 1889-1920+.
H *Ha'porth* 1891-93 > H *Comet* 1893-94.
H Dist *Advertiser* 1913-17.
H Boro' *Advertiser* 1913-20+.
See also Bradford, Halifax, Wakefield.

Hunslet *see Leeds.*

ILKLEY
I *Gazette* (Wharfedale) 1868-1920 [Bradford Central Lib, Ilkley Lib 1880-1918].
I *Free Press* (Addingham, Purley, Otley, Guisley, Yeadon) 1873-1920+.
See also Otley.

KEIGHLEY [KL = Keighley Lib]
K *News* (Bingley) 1862-1920+ [BCL, KL].
K *Herald* 1873-1911 [KL].
K *Chronicle* 1905-09 [KL].

Kippax *see Castleford.*

KNARESBOROUGH
Burniston's Northern *Luminary* 1849-53.
K *Times* (Harrogate, Ripley, Boroughbridge, Ripon, Claro) 1860-95.
K *Post* 1863-1920 (Boroughbridge) 1869-1920+.
See also Harrogate, Wetherby.

Knottingley *see Castleford.*
Laisterdyke *see Bradford.*

LEEDS [LCL = Leeds Central Lib]
L (& Yorks) *Mercury* pre1750-1920+ [LCL; Bradford Central Lib pre1750-1845; Wakefield Lib 1837-1904].
(Wright's) L *Intelligencer* 1754-1866 > Yorks *Post* 1866-1920+ [LCL; Morley Lib 1755-1866; Wakefield Lib 1865-1920+; York Minster Lib 1764-1815, 1822-23].
L *Correspondent* [LCL 1815-22].
L *Independent* 1819-25 [LCL 1820, 1825-26*].
L *Patriot* 1826-33 [LCL 1824-32*].
L *Times* 1833-1901 [LCL 1834-1901].
(Northern) *Star* (of Freedom) 1838-52 [Halifax Central Lib, LCL, Leics Record Office].
L (& West Riding) (Evening) *Express* 1857-1901 [LCL 1855-99].
L *Daily News* 1873-1905 [LCL 1874-1905].
Yorks *Independent* 1875-81.
National *Independent* 1876-89.
Yorks *Weekly Post* 1882-1920+ [LCL 1896-1920+].
Roundhay *Gazette* (Moorton, Shadwell, Seacroft, Thorner, Cross Gates) 1886-87 > Skyrack *Courier* 1889-1920+.
Hunslet & Holbeck *News* 1887-90 > South (& West) L *Echo* 1890-95.
(L/People's) Saturday *Journal* 1887-1907 [LCL 1884-1909*].
Yorks *Evening Post* 1890-1920+ [LCL 1896-1920+].
L *Express* 1894-99.
Yorks *Evening News* 1905-20+.
L *Budget* 1906-11.
Yorks *Weekly Record* 1909-10 [LCL 1909-20+].
L (& Dist) *Weekly Citizen* 1911-20+.
Weekly Post (Farsley, Calverley, Rodley) 1912-16.
New/North L *News* 1913-20+.
(The) *Outlook* 1915-20.

Liversedge *see Cleckheaton, Heckmondwike.*
Lofthouse (Loftus) *see Yorks N.R.: Guisborough.*
Malton *see Yorks N.R.*
Masborough *see Rotherham.*
Methley *see Castleford, Rothwell.*

MEXBOROUGH
M & Swinton *Times* 1877-1920+ [Barnsley Archives, Doncaster Lib, Rotherham Lib].
South Elmsall, South Kirkby & Hemsworth *Times* 1913-1920+.
See also Rawmarsh.

MIRFIELD
M & Ravensthorpe *Reporter* 1881-1920+.
M *Herald* (Ravensthorpe) 1919-20+.

Moorton *see Leeds.*

MORLEY
M *Reporter* 1868-75.
M *Observer* 1871-1920+ [Morley Lib].

NORMANTON
N, Altofts & Whitwood *Free Press* 1872-76.
N (& Altofts) *Guardian* 1880-83.

Yorkshire: West Riding *continued*

OSSETT [OL = Ossett Lib]
O *Observer* 1864-1920+ [OL, Wakefield Lib].

OTLEY
O *News* 1867-90.
O & Ilkley *Guardian* (Wharfedale) 1875-81.
Wharfedale & Airedale *Observer* 1880-1920+.
Wharfedale & Airedale *Standard* 1898-1901.
Wharfedale *Times* (Yeadon, Guiseley, Rawdon) 1919-20+.
See also Ilkley.

PENISTONE
P, Stocksbridge & Hoyland (& Ecclesfield) (& Chapeltown) *Express* 1898-1920+ [Barnsley Archives 1898-1917].

PONTEFRACT [PL = Pontefract Lib]
P *Telegraph* 1857-1902.
(Copley's) P (& Castleford) *Advertiser* 1858-1920+ [Castleford Lib, PL].
P & Castleford *Express* 1880-1920+ [Castleford Lib, PL].
P & Castleford Weekly *Herald* (Goldcross) 1892-1900.

PUDSEY
P & Stanningley *News* 1878-1920+.
P (Dist) *Advertiser* (Stanningley, Farsley) 1889-1920+.
(P) *Echo* 1896-1905 > P & Dist *Free Press* 1905 [Leeds Central Lib 1890-91].

Purley *see also Ilkley.*
Rastrick *see also Brighouse.*
Ravensthorpe *see Mirfield.*
Rawdon *see Otley.*

RAWMARSH
R (Swinton) & Mexbro' *Advertiser* 1903-20+.
See also Rotherham.

Ripley *see Harrogate.*

RIPON
R *Gazette* (Bedale, Northallerton) 1868-1920+
R & Richmond *Chronicle* (North Yorks, South Durham) 1870-93.
R *Observer* 1889-1920+.
R *Advertiser* 1911-20+.
See also Knaresborough; Yorks N.R.: Bedale, Richmond.

Rochdale *see under Lancs.*
Rodley *see Leeds.*

ROTHERHAM
R (& Masbro') *Advertiser* (South Yorks) 1858-1920+ [Rotherham Lib].
R *Journal* 1857-61.
R *Express* (Rawmarsh) 1896-1920+.
See also Sheffield.

ROTHWELL
R *Times* 1876-1911 [Rothwell Lib 1873-1911; Wakefield Lib 1883-87].
R (& Methley) *Free Press* 1890-1901.
R *Courier* 1913-20+ [Leeds Central Lib].

Roundhay *see Leeds.*
Saltaire *see Shipley.*
Scholes *see Cleckheaton.*
Seacroft *see Leeds.*

SELBY
S *Times* (Howdenshire, Goole) 1869-1920+.
S *Express* 1872-1920+.

Shadwell *see Leeds.*

SHEFFIELD [SL = Sheffield LS Lib]
(S) (Public) *Advertiser* 1760-93 [SL].
S *Register* 1787-94 [SL].
S *Courant* 1793-97 [SL 1796-97].
(S) *Iris* 1794-1850 [SL 1794-1856, index].
S *Mercury* 1808-48 [SL].
S (& Rotherham) (Daily) *Independent* 1819-1920+.
S *Courant* (Rotherham, Barnsley, Chesterfield) 1828-34 [SL 1827-34].
S *Patriot* 1838-41.
S *Times* 1846-74 [SL].
S *Free Press* (Rotherham, Barnsley) 1851-57 [SL].
S *Advertiser* 1853-56.
S Daily *Telegraph* 1855-1920+ [Wakefield Lib 1855-90; Rotherham Lib 1890-1920+].
S *Daily News* 1856-62 [SL 1856-57].
S *Argus* (South Yorks, North Derbys) 1858-61.
S (Daily) *Post* 1873-87.
S *Evening Star* 1874-88.
(S) *Weekly Telegraph* 1884-1920+.
S (& Rotherham) Weekly *Independent* 1884-1920.
(The) *Week* 1888-1902 > (S) *Weekly News* 1902-20+.
(S) Evening/Yorks *Telegraph* 1887-1920+.
(Sunday) *Week/Telegraph* 1898-1911.
Yorks *Early Bird* 1898-1920+.
S *Weekly News* 1899-1902.
S *Guardian* 1906-16 [SL 1906-11].
S *Mail* 1920+.

SHIPLEY
S (& Saltaire) *Times* (Airedale) 1876-1920+.
S *Express* (Airedale) 1894-1905.
(Watkin's) (S) (& Dist) *Advertiser* 1907-15.

Skyrack *see Leeds.*

SLAITHWAITE
S/Colne Valley *Guardian* 1896-1920+.

Snaith *see Yorks E.R.: Goole.*

SOUTH ELMSALL
SE/Hemsworth *Express* 1918-20+ [South Elmsall Lib, Wakefield Lib 1913-20+].
See also Mexborough.

South Kirkby *see Mexborough.*

SOWERBY BRIDGE
SB *Chronicle* 1884-1914 [HCL 1883-1914].

Spenborough *see Cleckheaton.*

Yorkshire: West Riding *continued*

Spen Valley *see Cleckheaton.*
Stanningley *see Pudsey.*
Stocksbridge *see Penistone.*
Swinton *see Mexborough, Rawmarsh.*

TADCASTER
T *Post* (East & West Yorks) 1861-79 > T *News* (Cawood) 1879-1920.
See also Wetherby.

THORNE
(Isle of Axholme &) T *Advertiser* 1873-94.
See also Doncaster.

Thorner *see Leeds.*
Todmorden *see under Lancs.*

WAKEFIELD [WL = Wakefield Lib]
W *Star* 1804 [WL 1803-11].
W & Halifax/Dewsbury *Journal* (Huddersfield) 1819-34 [WL 1811-34*].
W.R. *Herald*/W *Journal* 1835-1913 [WL 1836-1913].
W & W.R. *Examiner* 1849-52 [WL].

Yorkshire: West Riding: Wakefield *continued*

W *Express* 1852-1920+ [WL].
W *Free Press* 1860-1902 [WL 1860-1902*].
W *Echo* 1882-1906 [WL 1876-91].
W Free Press *Evening News* 1880-83.
W *Sentinel* 1898-1901.
W *Advertiser* 1906-20+ [WL].
See also Bradford, Halifax.

WETHERBY
W *News* (Central Yorks) 1857-1920+.
Northern *Reporter* (Knaresborough, Tadcaster) 1868-1916.

Wharfedale *see also Ilkley, Otley.*
Whitwood *see Castleford, Normanton.*

WOMBWELL
W *Guardian* 1902-11 [Barnsley Archives].

Wortley *see Armley.*
Yeadon *see Ilkley, Otley.*

For other newspapers covering Yorks W.R., see also Derbys: Eckington; Lancs: Colne; Notts: Worksop.

WALES

[NLW = The National Library of Wales, Aberystwyth, which houses the main collection of newspapers in Wales. In this edition Welsh language titles, omitted in the earlier edition, are now included.]

ANGLESEY
(Ynys Môn)

BEAUMARIS

B/Menai Bridge *Visitor* (Jul-Sep only) 1857-58, 1863-65, 1867 [Carnarvon RO; 1857-58, 1863; NLW 1857-67].

HOLYHEAD (Caergybi)

[ARO = Anglesey Record Office, Llangefni]

(Y) *Punch* Cymraeg [NLW 1858-64].

H (Weekly) *Mail* (Llandudno, Colwyn Bay) 1885-1920+ [ARO 1883-86, 1888-90, 1920+; NLW 1920+].

H *Chronicle* [ARO 1907-08, 1910-20+; NLW 1909-20+].

Menai Bridge see *Beaumaris.*

BRECONSHIRE
(Sir Frycheiniog)

BRECON (Aberhonddu) [BL = Brecon Library].

(The) *Silurian* (Cardiff, Merthyr) 1838-43, 1845-46, 1849-55 [BL 1838-55*; NLW 1838-43, 1845-46, 1850-1855].

B *Journal* 1855-68 [BL, NLW 1855-68].

B *Reporter* 1863-67 [BL, NLW].

B (& Radnor) *County Times* 1866-70, 1872-95, 1900 1920+ [BL 1866-96, 1898-1920+; NLW 1866-86, 1898-1909].

B *Free Press* 1883-85 > Brecknock *Beacon* 1885-96.

B & Radnor *Express* (Carmarthen) 1889-97, 1899-1920+ [NLW; Brecknock Museum, Brecon 1910-20+; Llandrindod Wells Lib 1889-1908].

See also Glam: Merthyr Tydfil; Monm: Newport.

Llanwrtyd see Radnors: Builth Wells, Llandrindod Wells.

Caernarvonshire see as Carnarvonshire, page 66.

CARDIGANSHIRE
(Ceredigion)

ABERYSTWYTH

A *Observer* 1869-76, 1878-95, 1898-1911, 1913-15 [NLW 1858-62, 1864-1915; Univ of Wales Bangor 1885, 1891-92, 1896, 1898-1902, 1909-14].

(A Despatch &) Cardigan Bay *Visitor* (Barmouth, Criccieth, Pwllheli) 1889-1916 [NLW 1891-1900].

Cardigan *County Times* & Shropshire & Mid-Wales Advertiser 1898-1907 [NLW 1881-83, 1897-1907].

A Visitors' *Gazette* [NLW 1905*, 1909*].

Welsh *Gazette* 1899-1920+ [NLW].

Cardiganshire *continued*

CARDIGAN (Aberteifi)

C *Herald* 1869-73 [NLW].

C & Tivy-side *Advertiser* 1870-1920+ [Ceredigion Archives, Aberystwyth 1866-1920+; NLW 1884-95, 1909-20+].

C *Observer* (Carms, Pembs) 1876-98 [NLW 1876-83, 1887-89, 1890-97*].

See also Aberystwyth; Pembs: Haverfordwest.

LAMPETER (Llanbedr pont Steffan)

(Y) *Brython* Cymreig 1892, 1894-1901 [Cardiff Central Lib, NLW 1892-1901].

CARMARTHENSHIRE

AMMANFORD (Rhydaman)

Amman Valley *Chronicle* (East Carms) 1913-20+ [NLW; Carmarthen Lib].

Amman Valley see *Ammanford; Glam: Loughor*

CARMARTHEN (Caerfyrddin)

(C) *Journal* 1817-1920+ [NLW; Carmarthen Lib 1810-1920+; Swansea Ref Lib 1844-75*, 1885-94*].

(The) *Welshman* 1832-71, 1873-95, 1897-1911, 1013 1920+ [Carmarthen Lib, NLW 1845-1920+].

Seren Cymru 1851-1920+ [NLW 1851, 1856-1920+; Swansea City Archives 1857-62*, 1891-93*, 1901; Swansea Ref Lib 1892-1920+; University of Wales Bangor 1856-1920+].

C *Weekly Reporter* 1860-1920+ [NLW 1860-70, 1871, 1873-1920+].

C *Express* 1876-78.

See also Brecons: Brecon.

LLANELLY (Llanelli)
[LL = Llanelly Lib]

L (& County) *Guardian* 1869-1920+ [LL 1863-1920+; NLW 1869-72, 1873-1920+].

South Wales *Press* 1869-1920+ [LL 1898, 1908-20+; NLW 1867-71, 1875-1920+.

Carms *Notes* > Carms *Miscellany* [Cardiff Central Lib, Carmarthen Lib, NLW, Swansea Ref Lib, University of Wales Bangor 1889-92].

L *Mercury* 1891-96, 1899-1911, 1912-20+ [LL 1891-95, 1897-1920+; NLW 1891-1920+].

L *Star* 1909-20+ [NLW 1910-13, 1916-20+].

L *Argus* 1911, 1913--20+ [NLW 1920+].

For other newspapers covering Carms, see also Cards: Cardigan.

WALES *continued*

CARNARVONSHIRE
(Sir Caernarfon)

[ARO = Anglesey Record Office, Llangefni; CRO = Carnarvon Record Office; DRO = Dolgellau (Merioneth) Record Office; NLW = National Library of Wales, Aberystwyth; SRL = Swansea Reference Library; UWA = University of Wales, Aberystwyth; UWB = University of Wales, Bangor.]

BANGOR

North Wales *Gazette* 1813, 1827, 1850 [ARO 1822-27; CRO 1808-27*; Hawarden (Flints) RO 1811-16; NLW 1808-21*, 1822-27; UWB 1808-27].

North Wales *Chronicle* 1827-73, 1875-95, 1897-1920+ [ARO 1829-30, 1903; CRO 1827-32, 1840-43*, 1850-1858, 1860-1920+; UWB 1827-31, 1833-34, 1838-41, 1851, 1853-58, 1893-1904, 1913].

(Y) *Cymro* 1848-66 [NLW, UWB].

Cronicl Cymru 1866-71 [NLW 1866-72; UWB 1866-71].

Llais y wlad 1874-84 [NLW; CRO 1874, 1876, 1879, 1881-84; UWB 1875, 1877-78].

Gwalia 1881-1920+ [UWB 1891-1900, 1902, 1906, 1909-11, 1913].

(Y) *Clorianydd* 1891-1920+ [ARO 1893-1907, 1909-15, 1917-20+; NLW 1897-1904, 1909-20+].

Chwarelwr Cymreig 1893-1902 [NLW 1893-96, 1898-1902; CRO 1898-1902].

Barmouth see Carnarvon; Cards: Aberystwyth.

CARNARVON (Caernarfon)

C (& Denbigh) *Herald* (Merioneth) 1831-1920+ [CRO 1831-72, 1874-83, 1885-86, 1888-90, 1893-1920+; NLW 1849-1920+; Ruthin (Denbs) RO 1831-82; SRL 1837-38*, 1885-93*; UWA 1831-82; UWB 1831-36, 1837-90, 1897, 1899, 1901, 1911].

Herald Cymraeg 1855-1920+ [UWB].

(Y) *Goleuad* 1869-1920+ [NLW; ARO 1869в74, 1876-1881, 1884-85, 1891-92, 1899-1900, 1902-20+; CRO 1869-1909, 1913, 1916-18, 1920+; DRO 1869-1906, 1919; SRL 1869-1920*; UWB 1869, 1871-1918].

(Y) *Darlunydd* 1876-79 [Cardiff Central Lib, NLW, SRL, UWB].

North Wales *Express* 1877-84 > North Wales *Observer* 1884-95, 1897-1920+ [CRO 1881-83*, 1893-1903; NLW 1878-93, 1895-1907, 1913-20+; UWB 1877-78, 1885-87, 1889-94, 1902-03, 1909-14].

Genedl (Cymreig) 1877-1920+.

Cards & Merioneth Herald 1885-88 > *Merioneth News* (Barmouth) 1888-1920+ [DRO 1887-90; NLW 1918-20+].

(Y) *Werin* 1889-96, 1898-1920+ [NLW 1885-1920+; UWB 1889-94, 1909].

Nelson [NLW, UWB 1890-97].

Papur Pawb 1893-1916 [CRO 1893-1900; NLW 1893-1917; UWB 1893-98, 1901].

(Yr) *Eco* Cymraeg 1899-1914 [NLW 1899-1900, 1905-1914].

(Y) *Wyntyll* 1903-20+ [NLW; ARO 1914-18].

Welsh *Leader* 1903-07 [NLW; CRO 1903-04*].

(Y) *Dinesydd* Cymreig 1912-20+ [NLW, UWB].

Conway (Conwy) *see Penmaenmawr.*

Criccieth (Cricieth) *see Carns: Aberystwyth.*

LLANDUDNO

(Original) L *Directory* 1855-72, 1874-1920+ [CRO 1861-1864, 1869, 1873-77, 1881-1906, 1912-20+; NLW 1909-1920+].

L *Register* 1857-58, 1863-96, 1898-1920+ [CRO 1857-1858, 1862-63, 1867-69, 1871-75, 1877-81, 1883-86, 1888].

L *Advertiser* 1885-95, 1898-1920+ [Conwy Archive Service, Llandudno 1885-95; CRO 1885-99, 1901-20+; Llandudno Lib 1896-1920+].

(The) *Pilot* 1914-20+.

See also Anglesey: Holyhead.

Llanfairfechan *see Penmaenmawr.*

PENMAENMAWR

(The) *Visitor* (Llanfairfechan, Conway Vale) 1888-91.

PORTHMADOG

(Yr) *Awr* 1908-12 [NLW 1908-12*].

PWLLHELI

(Yr) *Eifion/Arweinydd* 1856-60 [NLW, UWB 1856-59].

P *Chronicle* 1889-93 [NLW].

(Yr) *Udgorn* (Rhyddid) 1898-1920+ [NLW; CRO 1904-1913*].

For other newspapers covering Carn, see also Cards: Aberystwyth.

DENBIGHSHIRE
(Sir Ddinbych)

[NLW = National Library of Wales, Aberystwyth; RRO = Ruthin (Denbighshire) Record Office; UWB = University of Wales, Bangor.]

ABERGELE

A & Pensarn *Visitor* 1869-97, 1899-1920+ [Abergele Lib 1915-20+; NLW 1866-1920+*; RRO 1869-1920+].

A & Pensarn *Times* 1908-10, 1912-20+ [NLW 1920+].

CEFN

C *Chronicle* 1919-20+ [NLW 1913-20+; UWB 1915-16, 1918-20+].

Colwyn *see Colwyn Bay.*

COLWYN BAY (Bae Colwyn)

CB *Gazette* (Colwyn, Llandrillo) 1884-91.

CB & Colwyn *Visitor* 1889-93.

(CB &) Welsh Coast/North Wales *Pioneer* 1898-1920+ [Bodleian Lib, Oxford 1898-1915; Conway Archives Service, Llandudno; Colwyn Bay Lib; NLW 1909-20+].

(CB/North Wales) *Weekly News* 1889-1909; 1911, 1913-1920+ [Colwyn Bay Lib, RRO; Conway Archives Service 1892-1920+; Hawarden (Flints) RO 1889-1906; Llandudno Lib 1885-1920+].

CB *Halfpenny Herald* 1906-20+.

CB *Advertiser* 1920+ [NLW 1912-13*].

CB *Sentinel* 1913-16.

See also Anglesey: Holyhead.

WALES: Denbighshire *continued*

DENBIGH (Dinbych).

Baner (ar Amserau) Cymru 1857-1920+ [Cardiff Central Lib, NLW, UWB; Carnarvon RO 1857-86, 1000-95, 1899, 1901-03; Dolgellau (Merioneth) RO 1857-1903, 1912-20; Anglesey RO 1858-64, 1866-84, 1896; RRO 1857-95; Swansea Ref Lib 1857-1920*].

Udgorn y Bobi 1858-65 [NLW; UWB 1861-63*].

D/Denbs (Ruthin & Vale of Clwyd) *Free Press* (Flints) 1882-95, 1898-1920+ [Mold Lib, NLW, RRO].

North Wales *Times* 1895-96, 1899-1920+ [NLW, RRO 1895-1920+].

Llandrillo *see Colwyn Bay.*

LLANGOLLEN

L *Advertiser* 1868-72, 1874-1920 [NLW 1868-1920; RRO 1869-86, 1887-88*, 1889-1919].

Pensarn *see Abergele.*

RHOS

R *Herald* 1894-20+ [Rhos Lib; NLW 1894-1903, 1905-1920+; UWB 1894-1903, 1905-14, 1916-17, 1920+].

Ruthin (Ruthun) *see Denbigh.*

WREXHAM (Wrecsam)

[ML = Mold Lib; WL = Wrexham Lib]

W (Weekly) *Advertiser* 1854-1920+ [RRO; NLW 1850-1852, 1857-1920+; ML, WL 1850-52, 1857-1920+].

(The) *Wrexhamite* (Flintshire) 1855-56 > W/Denbs & Flints *Telegraph* (North Salop, West Ches) 1857-67 [RRO 1855-64].

W/North Wales *Guardian* (Flints) 1869-1920+ [NLW 1869-84, 1889, 1891, 1913-16, 1919-20+; RRO 1869-1884, 1907-08; ML, WL 1877-78, 1880-85, 1887, 1890-1920+].

W *Free Press* 1870-73.

Illus W *Argus* 1884-92, 1894-1900, 1902-16 [NLW 1886-89, 1912-15, WL 1884-1900, 1902-10].

W *Journal* 1913-17 [WL 1903-04*].

W *Leader* 1920+ [Bodleian Lib, Oxford, ML, NLW, WL].

See also Flints: Rhyl.

For other newspapers covering Denbs, see also Ches: Chester.

FLINTSHIRE
(Sir Fflint)

[CRO = Carnarvon Record Office, HRO = Hawarden (Flints) Record Office; NLW = National Library of Wales, Aberystwyth; UWB = University of Wales, Bangor.]

HOLYWELL (Treffynnon)

Flints *Observer* 1857-95, 1900-15, 1920 [CRO 1917-1920+; HRO 1857-95, 1897-1916, 1918-20+; NLW 1857-1920+;].

County *Herald* 1887-1920+ [HRO; Mold Lib 1898-1920+; NLW 1887-96, 1898-1920+; UWB 1887-1920+].

Flintshire *continued*

MOLD (Yr Wyddgrug)

Y *Protestant* 1839-48 [NLW].

County *Leader* 1908-09 [NLW 1910-20+].

Flints *News* 1909-11, 1912-13 [HRO, NLW 1909-13]

PRESTATYN

P *Weekly* 1908-20+ [HRO 1905-20+; NLW 1905-12, 1920+].

RHYL

R *Record* 1855-86 [HRO 1858-69, 1874-1920+; NLW 1858-69, 1874-86; Rhyl Lib 1856-1920+].

R *Visitor* 1857-63 [CRO 1857-58, 1862-65].

(Y) *Dywysogaeth* 1870-81 > Y *Llan* (a'r dywysogaeth) 1881, 1884-1920+ [NLW 1873-79*, 1881, 1884-1909; UWB 1870-81].

(R) *Journal* 1870-1920+ [HRO 1866-75, 1878-1920+; NLW 1899-1920+; Rhyl Lib 1889-1920+].

(Y) *Gwyliedydd* 1877-91, 1893-1909 [NLW 1877-1909; UWB 1892-1920+].

R *Guardian* (Wrexham) 1878-1920+ [NLW 1890].

(R) *Record/Advertiser* 1880-1911, 1913-20+ [HRO; NLW 1878-1917, 1919-20; Rhyl Lib 1887-1920].

R *News* 1901-05.

R *Pilot* [NLW 1911-14*].

For other newspapers covering Flint, see also Ches: Chester; Denbs: Denbigh, Wrexham.

GLAMORGAN
(Morgannwg)

[BdL = Bridgend Lib; CCL = Cardiff Central Library; GA = Glamorgan Archives, Cardiff; MTL = Merthyr Tydfil Library; NCL = Newport Central Library; NLW = National Library of Wales, Aberystwyth; SRL = Swansea Reference Library; UWB = University of Wales Bangor; UWS = University of Wales, Swansea.]

Aberavon *see Bridgend.*

ABERDARE (Aberdâr)

[ACL = Aberdare Central Library]

(Y) *Gwron* (Cymreig/a'r gweithiwr) 1852-60 [ACL, CCL, NLW].

(Y) *Gwladgarwr* 1858-82 [NLW; CCL 1860-82].

A *Times* (Merthyr, Hirwaun, Mountain Ash, Pontypridd, Vale of Neath, Rhondda Valleys, Cardiff) 1869-76, 1878-96, 1898-1902 [ACL, NLW 1861-1902; CCL 1861-79, 1884, 1887, 1896, 1900-02].

Tarlan y Gweithiwr 1884-96, 1890-1900, 1002-10, 1912-1914 > (Y) *Darian* 1914-20+ [ACL 1875-78, 1882, 1888, 1908, 1911; CCL, NLW 1875-1920+; SRL 1875-1920+; Treorchy Lib 1884-1920].

Gweithiwr Cymreig 1885-89.

A *Leader* 1902-20+ [ACL, NLW; Cynon Valley Lib 1902-1911].

A (& Mountain Ash Weekly) *Post* 1906-20 [NLW 1909-1912, 1914-20].

See also Merthyr Tydfil, Pontypridd.

BARGOED
(New Tredegar) B (& Caerphilly) *Journal* 1904-12 [Bargoed Library].

BARRY (Barri) [BrL = Barry Library]
B & Cadoxton *Journal* 1889-91 [BrL 1888-91].

B Dock *News* 1892-95, 1897-1909, 1911-1920+ [BrL 1889-1920+; CCL 1891].

B *Herald* 1896, 1898-1911, 1913-20+ [BrL 1896-1920+; NLW 1909-20+].

South Wales *Star* 1891-94 [BrL, NLW; CCL 1891-93].

BRIDGEND (Pen-y-bont)
[BdL = Bridgend Library]
B (& Neath) *Chronicle* (Cowbridge, Llantrisant Mercury, Maesteg, Aberavon, Taibach) 1857-68, 1880-94 [BdL, NLW 1857-68].

Central Glam *Gazette* 1866-94 [BdL].

Glam *Gazette* 1894-1920+ [BdL; CCL 1916-20+; NLW 1894-95, 1897-98, 1900-20+].

Chronicle for South & Mid Glam 1895-1912 [NLW 1897-1898*, 1914].

Glam *Gazette* (Aberavon, Port Talbot & district ed.) 1912-20+.

See also Radnors: Builth Wells.

Cadoxton *see Barry.*

CAERPHILLY (Caerffili)
Caerphilly Journal 1914-20+.

See also Bargoed, Pontypridd; Monm: Rhymney .

CARDIFF (Caerdydd)
[CCL = Cardiff Central Lib]
South Wales *Times* 1857-61.

C *Times* 1857-1920+ [CCL 1860-1920+; NLW 1864, 1866, 1869, 1871-73, 1878-1920+; SRL 1912-20+].

C (Swansea & Newport) Shipping & Mercantile *Gazette* 1869-1892, 1894-1911 [NLW 1883-85*].

Western *Mail* 1869-1920+ [Bridgend Lib 1914-20+; CCL 1869-1920*; GA 1872-1920+; NLW 1869-71, 1873, 1874-95, 1897-99, 1908-20+; NCL 1903-20+; SRL 1869-71, 1873-95, 1897-1910, 1912-20+].

(C) *Weekly Mail* 1870-95, 1897, 1899-1910, 1912-20+ [GA 1870-1920*; NLW 1911-20+].

South Wales (Daily) *News* 1872-1920+ [CCL, NCL, NLW; GA 1885-1914*; UWB 1887-88, 1905-20+].

C *Free Press* 1876-84.

(The) *Principality* 1877-80.

Roath *Chronicle* (Splotland) 1878-84.

C & South Wales *Whip* 1886-88 > C *Figaro* 1901-03 [CCL 1886-93, 1901-03*; NLW 1886-88*].

News of the Week 1888-95 [CCL 1889-94; NLW 1891-1892].

(South Wales) *Evening Express* 1887-95, 1899-1910, 1912-1920+ [CCL 1887-1920+; NLW 1891-1920+].

C *Advertiser* 1891-94.

South Wales *Echo* 1889-1909, 1911-20+ [Bargoed Lib, CCL 1887-1920+; GA 1885-1920*; NLW 1894, 1896-1897, 1912, 1917-20+].

C/South Wales *Journal of Commerce* 1904-20+ [NLW 1909-20+].

Ward's *Weekly* 1906-14.

Kemp's Local *Gazette* 1914-20+.

C & District/South Wales *Advertiser* 1920+.

See Brecons: Brecon; Monm: Newport.

Cogan *see Penarth.*

Dowlais *see Merthyr Tydfil.*

Garw *see Maesteg, Rhondda.*

Gelligaer *see Bargoed.*

Glamorgan *see Monm: Newport.*

Gower *see Swansea.*

Hirwuan *see Aberdare.*

Llantrisaint *see Pontypridd.*

Llynfi *see Maesteg.*

LOUGHOR (Casllwchwr)
South Wales *Observer* (Amman Valley) 1889-92 [NLW 1889-92*].

MAESTEG
Glam *Advertiser* (Llynfi, Ogmore, Garw, Avon Valleys) 1919-20+ [Bridgend Lib].

See also Rhondda.

MERTHYR TYDFIL (Merthyr Tudful)
[MTL = Merthyr Tydfil Lib]
Glamorgan, Monmouth & Brecon *Gazette* 1833-41 > Cardiff & M *Guardian* 1845-74 [Aberdare Central Lib, Bridgend Lib 1833-74; MTL 1833-35, 1839-49, 1854-1873; NLW 1832-41, 1843-51, 1853-65, 1867-74].

M *Telegraph* 1858-81 [MTL, NLW 1855-81].

M *Star* (Dowlais, Aberdare) 1859-65, 1867-72 [NLW 1859, 1860-72*].

M *Express* 1864-97, 1899-1910, 1912-20+ [MTL; Ceredigion Archives, Aberystwyth 1873, 1898, 1911-1920*; NCL 1892-1920+; NLW 1864-69, 1871-74*, 1901-20+].

(Y) *Fellten* 1868-73, 1874-76 [MTL 1868-76].

(Y) *Tyst* (a'r dydd) 1871-1920+ [NLW; GA 1892-1916, 1920+; UWB 1874-87, 1892-1920+].

M *Times* (Dowlais) 1871-73 [MTL, NLW].

Workmen's *Advocate* 1873-75 [MTL].

M/Dowlais *Times* (Aberdare, Pontypridd) 1891-99 [MTL, NLW].

M *Guardian* (Dowlais) 1906-08 [MTL, NLW].

(The) *Pioneer* 1913-20+ [NLW 1911-22].

See also Aberdare, Pontypridd.

MOUNTAIN ASH (Aberpennar)
MA *Post* 1912-20.

See also Aberdare, Pontypridd.

Mumbles (Mwmbwls) *see Swansea.*

NEATH (Castell-Nedd)
N *Gazette* 1889-1911 > Mid-Glam *Herald* 1911-14 [NLW 1909-14; SRL 1892].

Vale of N *Advertiser* 1914 [NLW 1910-12*].

See also Aberdare, Swansea.

Ogmore *see Maesteg, Rhondda.*

PENARTH
P *Times* 1898-1920+ [NLW 1909-20+].

P *Chronicle* (Cogan) 1889-94, 1896 [GA, NLW 1895; Penarth Lib 1920+].

P *Advertiser* 1914-16.

PONTARDAWE
West Wales *Observer* 1919-20+.

PONTYPRIDD [PL = Pontypridd Lib]
P Dist *Herald* (Rhondda Valley, Llantrisant, Caerphilly, Mountain Ash) 1878-94 [Treorchy Lib 1878-80, 1884, 1891-94].

P (& Rhondda Valleys) *Chronicle* 1882-1905 [CCL 1881-1905; NLW 1881-99, 1901-02, 1905; PL 1878-1884*, 1890-94].

Glam *Free Press* (Rhondda) 1891-1920+ [BdL 1891-1919*; CCL 1891-92; NLW 1896-99, 1909-20+; PL 1891-99, 1902-08, 1910-17, 1919].

(P) *Observer* 1897-1920+ [BdL, NLW, PL].

Glam (County) *Times* (Rhondda, Merthyr, Aberdare, Rhymney Valley) 1897-1920+ [BdL 1917-20+; NLW 1895-1900, 1909-20+; PL 1912, 1917-20+].

(Mid-)Rhondda *Gazette* 1913-20+ [NLW 1918-20+].

Rhondda Fach *Gazette* 1916-20+.

See also Aberdare, Merthyr Tydfil.

Port Talbot *see Bridgend.*

PORTH
P *Gazette* 1900-20+ [GA, NLW 1910-20+; Pontypridd Lib 1900-02].

PORTHCAWL
P *News* 1910-20+.

RHONDDA
R *Chronicle* 1884-98.

R *Leader* (Maesteg, Garw, Ogmore) 1899-1920+ [BdL, NLW, Pontypridd Lib, Treorchy Lib].

R Fach *Gazette* 1916-20+ [NLW 1918-20+].

See also Aberdare, Pontypridd.

Roath *see Cardiff.*

Splotland *see Cardiff.*

SWANSEA (Abertawe)
[SRL = Swansea Reference Lib; SM = Swansea Museum]

(The) *Cambrian* 1813-1920+ [CCL 1804-93; NLW 1804-1920+; SM 1804-85, 1888-93, 1896-1901, 1906-09, 1914-15; SRL 1804-93 (indexed 1804-70); UWB 1809-1826, UWS 1004-1918*].

S & Glam *Herald* 1847-90 [NLW 1847-51, 1854-90; SM 1847-66; SRL 1859-66, 1881-90*].

S & Neath *Advertiser* 1849-52 [NLW, SRL].

S *Journal* 1855-90 [NLW; SM 1843-44, 1852-57; SRL 1883-90].

S *Mercury* 1860-63.

(The) *Ferret*/South Wales *Ratepayer* 1870-79 [NLW 1870-72].

Cambria(n) *Daily Leader* 1861-1920+ [NLW; SM 1884-1890; SRL 1881-1920+*].

South Wales *Critic* 1869, 1888 [Ceredigion Archives, Aberystwyth], CCL 1869; NLW, SRL 1000-88].

S *Boy* [CCL 1884; NLW, SRL 1878-84*; UWS 1878-79, 1883-84].

Herald of Wales (Monm) 1882-90 > S & Glamorgan *Herald* 1891-1920+ [NLW 1911-19; SM 1859-60; SRL 1888-1920+].

Mumbles *Chronicle* (Gower) 1887, 1889-90 [NLW, SRL 1887-90].

Welsh Industrial *Times* 1888-98 [NLW, SRL].

S *Gazette*/S Daily *Shipping Register* 1888-1915* [NLW 1909-16; SRL 1890-1900].

Mumbles *Observer* (Gower) 1889-92 [NLW; SRL 1889-90].

South Wales *Radical* 1890 > South Wales *Liberal* 1890-1893 > S *Journal* 1893-94, 1899-1902 [NLW; CCL 1892-93].

(Daily) Industrial *World* 1892-97 [SRL 1892-98].

South Wales *Daily Post* 1893-1920+ [NLW 1893-95, 1897-98, 1899-1910; SRL 1893-95, 1897-1920+].

South Wales *Weekly Post* 1893-1920+ [NLW 1894, 1909-20+; SRL 1893-1900, 1903-04, 1908-19].

South Walian [SM 1896-1902].

Mumbles (Weekly) *Press* (Gower) 1905, 1911-14 [NLW 1909-20+; SRL 1903-15, 1917, 1919-20+].

See also Cardiff.

MERIONETH
(Meirionnydd)

[CA = Ceredigion Archives, Aberystwyth; DRO = Dolgellau (Merioneth) Record Office; NLW = National Library of Wales, Aberystwyth; UWB = University of Bangor, Wales.]

BALA (Y Bala)
(Y) *Brytwn* 1837-40 [NLW].

Meri *Herald/Standard* 1860-68 > Cambrian *News* 1869-1896, 1898-1920+ [Bodleian Lib, Oxford 1897-1920+; CA 1869-1920+; DRO 1881; NLW 1860-67*, 1869-1920+; Oswestry Lib 1865-66, 1868, 1870, 1876-77; UWB 1870, 1873-77, 1879-80, 1882-1903].

(Y) *Celt* (Newydd) 1878-1906 [NLW; Swansea Ref Lib 1882-90, UWD 1878-1906].

(Yr) *Eryr* 1894-98 [NLW; DRO 1895, 1898].

(Y) *Seren* 1889-92, 1894-1920+ [DRO 1898-99, 1902-1904, 1915-18, 1920+; NLW 1885-1907, 1917-20+]

BARMOUTH (Y Bermo)
B (& County) *Advertiser* 1878-89 [NLW 1878-96, 1899-1920+].

BLAENAU FFESTINIOG
(Y) *Rhedegydd* 1885-1920+ [DRO 1879, 1917-20+; NLW 1878-1902*, 1905-20+; UWB 1906, 1908-11, 1914].

(Y) *Glorian* 1899-1913.

(Yr) *Aelwyd* 1913-17 [NLW 1911-17*].

Gwyliedwd newydd 1910-20+.

WALES: Merioneth *continued*

CORRIS
(Y) *Negesydd* 1895-1909 [NLW 1895-1908].

CORWEN
(Yr) *Wythnos* (a'r Eryr) 1892, 1894-1920+ [NLW 1880-1881, 1892-98, 1909-20+].

(Yr) *Adsain* 1905-20+ [NLW].

DOLGELLAU
(Y) *Dydd* 1869-70, 1871-1920+ [DRO 1868-6, 1913-20+; NLW 1868-70, 1872-90, 1892-1920+; UWB 1869-70, 1873, 1875-1920+].

(Y) *Cymro* 1914-20+ [NLW, UWB; Swansea Ref Lib 1916-20*].

Merioneth (Meirionnydd) *see Carn: Carnarvon.*

TOWYN (Tywyn)
T-on-Sea & Merioneth County *Times* 1895-1905 [NLW].

For other Merioneth newspapers, see also Cards: Aberystwyth.

MONMOUTHSHIRE (Gwent)
(Sir Fynwy)

[GRO = Gwent (Monmouths) Record Office, Cwmbran; NCL = Newport Central Library; NLW = National Library of Wales, Aberystwyth.]

ABERGAVENNY
A *Chronicle* 1871-81, 1883-1910, 1912-1920+ [GRO 1874-1920+; NLW 1909-20+].

A *Mail* 1904-11, 1913 [NLW 1909-14].

ABERTILLERY (Abertileri)
South Wales *Gazette* (Newport) 1888-95, 1898-1920+ [NCL 1888-1920+; NLW 1909-20+].

Bargoed *see Rhymney.*

BRYNMAWR
B *Reporter* 1905-14.

CHEPSTOW [Casgwent]
[CL = Chepstow Lib]
C *Weekly Advertiser* 1855-1916 [CL; NCL 1855-78, 1883-1906, 1898-1916].

C (& County) *Mercury* (Glos) 1863-74.

C *Chronicle* 1884, 1886-88.

MONMOUTH (Mynwy)
Monm *Beacon* 1837-72, 1874-95, 1897-1920+ [Chepstow Lib 1837-85; Monmouth Museum 1837-1920+; NLW 1837-95, 1897-1920+].

Monm *Gazette* (Coleford, Forest of Dean) 1849-52 [NCL, NLW].

See also Newport; Glos: Coleford; Glam: Merthyr Tydfil.

Monmouthshire *continued*

NEWPORT (Casnewydd)
[NCL = Newport Central Lib]
Monm *Merlin* 1829-91 [NCL, NLW; Chepstow Lib 1837-1885*].

Monm *Advertiser* 1840-41 [NCL].

Star of Gwent (Monmouth, Glamorgan, Brecon) 1853-88 > South Wales *Times* 1888-1903 [NCL, NLW].

South Wales *Times* (Cardiff) 1857-58, 1861.

N/Weekly *Gazette* 1857-72 > South Wales Weekly *Telegram* 1872-91 [NCL 1857-81, 1888-91].

N *Free Press* 1869-74 [NCL].

(South Wales) Evening/Daily *Telegram* 1870-91 [NCL].

Evening Star of Gwent 1877-89 > South Wales *Daily Times* 1889-92 > South Wales *Daily Star* 1892-1901 > South Wales/N & Monm Daily/Evening *Telegraph* 1901-03 [NCL 1877-1902].

South Wales (Weekly) *Argus* 1892-1920+ [NCL; NLW 1909-20+].

Monm *Evening Post* 1908-20+ [Bodleian Lib, Oxford 1908-20+; NCL; NLW 1910-16].

Monm *Weekly Post* 1908-20+ [Bodleian Lib, Oxford; NCL 1909-20+; NLW 1916-20+].

See also Abertilery; Glos: Bristol; Glam: Cardiff.

PONTYPOOL (Pontypwl)
P/Monm *Free Press* 1879-1920+ [GRO 1859-71, 1881-1884, 1889-98, 1904-10, 1912-19; NCL 1859-96, 1898-1920+; NLW 1909-20+].

Raglan *see Usk.*

RHYMNEY (Rhymni)
(West) Monmouth *Guardian* (Bargoed, Caerphilly) 1896, 1898-1920+.

TREDEGAR
T *Times* 1869-77.

Weekly News 1877-84.

See also Glam: Bargoed.

USK (Brynbuga)
(Illustrated) U/County *Observer* (Raglan) 1855-95, 1897-1908 [GRO 1863-76, 1878; NCL 1856-1908; NLW 1855-67, 1892, 1894-1907].

U *Advertiser* 1907-19 [NCL 1919; NLW 1913-16].

For other Monm newspapers, see also Glos: Lydney; Herefs: Hereford; Glam: Swansea.

MONTGOMERYSHIRE
(Sir Drefaladwyn)

[NLW = National Library of Wales, Aberystwyth.]

LLANIDLOES
Radnors *Observer* 1869, 1875-76 [NLW].
(L) (& Newtown) Mid-Wales *Telegraph* 1869, 1877-84.
Mont (& Radnor) *Echo* 1887-1912.

NEWTOWN (Y Drenewydd)
N & Welshpool/Mont *Express* (Radnor) 1869-95, 1898-1920+ [Newtown Lib 1869-1920+; NLW 1909-20+].

WELSHPOOL (Y Trallwng)
Mont County *Times* (Salop) 1893-1920+ [Newtown Lib].

PEMBROKESHIRE
(Sir Benfro)

[NLW = National Library of Wales, Aberystwyth; PmRO = Pembs Record Office, Haverfordwest.]

Clynderwen see Narberth.
Dewsland see Haverfordwest.

FISHGUARD (Abergwaun)
County *Echo* 1894-1920+ [Fishguard Lib 1892-1920+; PmRO 1890-1920*; NLW 1901-20+].

HAVERFORDWEST (Hwlffordd)
(The) *Principality* 1848-50 [Cardiff Central Lib 1848-50*; NLW 1847-50].
Dewsland & Kernes/Pembroke County *Guardian* (Cardigan) 1869-71, 1873-96, 1898-1920+ [NLW 1867-82*, 1906-20+; PmRO 1869-82, 1890-1920+; Tenby Museum 1898-1920*].
H & Milford Haven/Pembs *Telegraph* 1854-96, 1898-1910, 1911-1920+ [PmRO 1854-1920+*; NLW 1857-1908*, 1909-20+].
Pembs *Herald* 1844-1920+ [Haverfordwest Lib, NLW; PmRO 1844-1920*].
Potter's Electric *News* 1855-1869 > Potter's *Newspaper* (Milford) 1871-72.

Kernes see Haverfordwest.

MILFORD HAVEN (Aberdaugleddau)
MH *Weekly News* 1904-06 [Haverfordwest Lib 1905-06].
MH & Neyland *Gazette* 1909-20 [NLW].
See also Haverfordwest, Pembroke.

NARBERTH (Arberth)
N, Whitland & Clynderwen *Weekly News* 1906-20+ [PmRO 1910-20*].

Neyland see Milford Haven, Pembroke.

PEMBROKE (Penfro)
Pembs *Advertiser* 1871-75.
P Dock & Tenby/P *Gazette* 1874-1920 [NLW 1909-12, 1914-15, 1918-20].
Ward-Davies's *Free Press* (Milford) 1880-95, 1897-1920+ [NLW 1909-20+].
P Dock *Journal* (Tenby, Milford Haven) 1901-07.
(P Dock, P & Neyland) *News* in a Nutshell 1912-20+ [NLW 1906-20+].

TENBY (Dinbych y Pysgod)
(The) *Tenby* 1869-74 > T *Times* 1874-76.
T & County *News* 1893-1919 [NLW 1893-96, 1898-1901, 1903-12; Tenby Museum 1893-1912].
T (& Pembroke Dock) *Observer* 1853-92, 1895-1910, 1913-20+ [NLW 1854-88*, 1889-1920+].
T *Telephone* 1879-85 > Pembs *Times* 1885-96, 1898-1911, 1913-18.
See also Pembroke.

Whitland see Narberth.

For other Pembs newspapers, see also Cards: Cardigan.

RADNORSHIRE
[NLW = National Library of Wales, Aberystwyth.]

BUILTH WELLS (Llanfair ym Muallt)
B, Llandrindod & Llanwrtyd *Advertiser* (Rhayader, Bridgend, Nantmel) 1886-87* [NLW 1871-92*].
See also Llandrindod Wells.

LLANDRINDOD WELLS
Radnors *Advertiser* (Builth Wells, Llanwrtyd) [NLW 1889-95*].
Radnor *Express* 1898-1920+ [NLW; Llandrindod Wells Lib 1906, 1908].
Radnors *Standard* 1898-1901 > Central Wales *News* 1901-19 > Mid-Wales *Independent* News 1919-20+ [NLW; Llandrindod Wells Lib 1899, 1906-07].
LW *Visitor* [NLW 1904-10*].
See also Builth Wells.

Nantmel see Builth Wells.
Radnor see Llandrindod Wells; Brecons: Brecon; Mont: Llanidloes, Newtown.
Rhayader (Rhyadyr) see Builth Wells.

For other newspapers covering Radnors, see also Herefs: Leominster, Kington; Mont: Llanidloes.

CHANNEL ISLANDS

Alderney see Guernsey.

GUERNSEY (Guernesey)

[GA = Guille'Alles Library, St. Peter Port; PL = Priaulx Library, St. Peter Port.]

Gazette de G 1837-1920+ [GA 1791-99, 1806-1920+; PL 1812-50, 1863-1910*].

(Le) *Mercure* de G/*Courier* de St.-Pierre Port [GA 1819-1826; PL 1810-16, 1830-32].

The *Star* 1869-1920+ [GA 1820-24, 1831-1920+; PL 1814-15, 1825-28].

(L') *Independence* [GA 1817-35; PL 1824-27].

(The) *Comet* 1839-97 [GA 1834-97].

G *Mail* 1869-71, 1873-91, 1898-99 [GA 1882-98].

G *Magazine* [GA, PL 1872-94].

G *Advertiser*/Weekly *Star* 1872-1920+ [GA 1882-1914].

Clarke's G *News* 1873-1905 [GA 1882-1903].

G *Independent* (Alderney, Sark, Herm) 1889-92.

(The) *Sun* 1890-97 [GA].

G *Moon* 1894-97.

G *Evening Press* 1897-1920+ [GA].

G *Weekly Press* 1897-98, 1902-20+.

Herm see Guernsey.

JERSEY

[SHL = St. Helier Central Library; SJ = Société Jersiaise, Lord Coulanche Library, St. Helier.]

Gazette de l'Ile de Jersey 1786-88 [SHL 1786-93, 1795-1808, 1813-16, 1819-34; SJ 1786-96].

Chronique(s) de J 1814-15, 1820-21, 1825-28, 1830-44, 1846-47, 1849-54, 1856-58, 1862, 1875-1920+ .

(Le) *Constitutionnel* [SHL 1820-76; SJ 1820-43, 1845-1849, 1853-54].

J *Loyalist* [SJ 1825-31].

(L') *Impartial* (de J) [SHL 1831-52, 1855-57; SJ 1831-41].

J *Times* [SJ 1832-35].

(Impartial et le) *Jersais* [SHL 1838-42; SL 1838-43].

(Le) *Miroir* [SJ 1840-42; SHL 1843-46].

British Press 1857, 1870-88 > J *Times* 1888-1910 [SHL 1848-1910].

(La) *Patrie* [SHL, SJ 1849-52].

J *Independent* 1855-75 > J *Weekly Press* 1875-1910 > J *Weekly Post* 1910-20+ [SHL 1856, 1858-63, 1876-1882; SJ 1858-63].

Nouvelle chronique de J 1859, 1865-66, 1873-75, 1889-1917 [SJ 1855-1917; SHL 1855-1916].

J *Express* 1866-1901 [SHL 1883-1901].

J General *Weekly Advertiser* [SHL 1869-78].

Weekly Express 1869-1901.

J *Observer* 1875-77, 1882-94*.

Evening Post 1897, 1899-1920+ [SHL 1905-20+].

Morning News 1909-20+ [SHL].

J Illus *Weekly* 1911-17.

(The) *Jerseyman* [SHL 1911-14].

Sark see Guernsey.

ISLE OF MAN

[DL = Douglas Library; MNH = Manx National Heritage Museum, Douglas.]

Note: MNH holdings are almost completely indexed from 1793 to 1845.

DOUGLAS

Manks *Mercury* [MNH 1793-95].

Manks *Advertiser* 1830 [DL 1802-06, 1811-22, 1825-26, 1828-31, 1837; MNH 1801-42].

IoM *Gazette* [MNH 1812-15].

Manx *Patriot* [MNH 1824-25].

Manx *Sun* 1838-1906 [DL 1837-40, 1845-84, 1892-1908; MNH 1821-1906].

Mona's *Herald* 1839, 1857-1920+ [DL 1838-40, 1843-46, 1850-80, 1891-1920+; MNH 1833-1920+].

Manx *Liberal* 1839 [MNH 1836-50].

IoM *Times* [MNH 1847-50].

IoM (Weekly) *Times* 1869-1920+ [MNH; DL 1867-83, 1888-89, 1891-93, 1895-99, 1901-20+].

IoM *Examiner* 1889-1920+ [Bodleian Lib, Oxford 1901-1920; DL 1880-87; MNH 1880-1920+].

(The) *Manxman* 1895-1900 [MNH].

IoM *Daily Times* 1898-1920+.

Manx *Patriot* [DL 1906-09].

PEEL

P City *Guardian* 1882-1920+ [MNH; DL 1895-1900, 1906-11, 1913-20+].

RAMSEY

R *Weekly News* 1889-1904 [MNH; DL 1896-1900].

R *Courier* 1889-1920+ [DL 1895-96, 1898-99, 1906-07, 1910-11, 1913-14, 1919-20+; MNH 1889, 1891-96, 1898-1920]